SPELL IT- WRITE!

Karen R. Harris, Ed.D.
Professor
Education
University of Maryland

Steve Graham, Ed.D.
Professor
Education
University of Maryland

Jerry Zutell, Ph.D.
Professor
Elementary Education and Reading
The Ohio State University

J. Richard Gentry, Ph.D.
Professor
Elementary Education and Reading
Western Carolina University

Gr. 2

Zaner-Bloser, Inc.
Columbus, Ohio

Contributing Author
Richard Lutz, Ph.D.
Adjunct Professor,
Applied Linguistics
Georgetown University
Washington, D.C.

Program Consultants
A. John Dalmolin, II
Director of Curriculum
Alhambra School District
Phoenix, Arizona

Gladys Hillman-Jones
Educational Consultant
South Orange, New Jersey

Jean Mann
Educational Consultant
Sharon, New Hampshire

Robert McGrattan
Elementary Principal
Asheville, North Carolina

Grade Level Consultants
María A. Alanis
Chapter I Instructional Coordinator
Austin, Texas

Ella Bell
Sixth Grade Teacher
Shepherdstown, West Virginia

Beverly Bennett
Fourth Grade Teacher
Booneville, Mississippi

Patricia Boyd
Seventh Grade Teacher
Cheektowaga, New York

Claudia Cornett, Ph.D.
Professor, Education
Wittenberg University
Springfield, Ohio

Deborah S. Daniels
Fifth Grade Teacher
Portsmith, Virginia

Michelle Gagin
Kindergarten Teacher
Columbus, Ohio

Marlene Goodman
Second Grade Teacher
Dyer, Indiana

Dominic F. Gullo, Ph.D.
Professor, Early Childhood
  Education
University of Wisconsin-Milwaukee
Milwaukee, Wisconsin

Nancy Hamlet
Second Grade Teacher
Peoria, Arizona

Janice T. Jones
Pre-kindergarten Teacher
Chicago, Illinois

Denise Larson
Third Grade Teacher
Portland, Oregon

Debra M. Leatherwood
Third Grade Teacher
Candler, North Carolina

Cathy Maloney
Fifth Grade Teacher
Boise, Idaho

Peter Monether
Middle School Teacher
Fitzwilliam, New Hampshire

Cheryl Prescott
First Grade Teacher
Brandon, Florida

Anita Ross
Kindergarten Teacher
Detroit, Michigan

Janet Strong
Eighth Grade Teacher
West Point, Mississippi

Mary Thomas Vallens
Fourth Grade Teacher
Irvine, California

Wanda Woods
First Grade Teacher
Detroit, Michigan

Sources for word histories and etymologies include:
Ayto, John. *Dictionary of Word Origins*. New York: Arcade Publishing, 1990.
Barnhart, Robert K., ed. *The Barnhart Dictionary of Etymology*. New York: The H.W. Wilson Company, 1988.
Claiborne, Robert. *The Roots of English*. New York: Anchor Books, Doubleday, 1989.

Spell It—Write! referred to *Webster's Ninth New Collegiate Dictionary* in the development of these materials.
Webster's Ninth New Collegiate Dictionary. Springfield, MA: Merriam-Webster Inc., 1988.

Design:
Brock Waldron, Bill Smith Studio

Illustration:
Clay art and pages 99 and 117 by Jackie Snider. Logos and Meeting My Goal art by Brock Waldron. All other illustrations by Chip Wass.

Speller's Workouts:
Ron Leiser

Photography:
Page 23 by W. Jacobs/Superstock. Page 39 by Don Fleming/Tony Stone Images. Page 47 by Peter Miller/The Image Bank. Page 83 by James Carmichael/The Image Bank. Page 92 by Schuster/Superstock. Page 125 by Elyse Lewin/The Image Bank. Page 141 by Murray Alcosser/The Image Bank. All other photographs by Ken Karp.

ISBN: 0-88085-406-5

Zaner-Bloser, Inc., P.O. Box 16764, Columbus, Ohio 43216-6764

Printed in the United States of America

96 97 98 WC 5

SPELL IT— WRITE!

TABLE OF CONTENTS

A Week With *Spell It—Write!*

MY WORD LIST

job

leg

nut

set

bad

Getting to Know *Spell It—Write!*

Sentences

1. My mother has a new **job**.

2. This old teddy bear has only one **leg**.

3. We watched the squirrel hide a **nut**.

4. Would you please **set** the table?

5. It's too **bad** the library is closed.

Are my words spelled right?

10 Practice Unit

Monday

These are the sentences to use for pretests.

Tuesday

Write words your teacher gives you and other words you want to learn here.

Check the spelling of all the words you write!

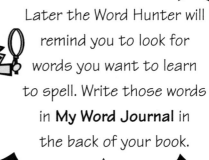

Later the Word Hunter will remind you to look for words you want to learn to spell. Write those words in **My Word Journal** in the back of your book.

Tuesday

The **Big Idea** tells you what the spelling unit is about.

BIG IDEA!

I can help myself learn to spell with *Spell It—Write!*

Taking Your Spelling Test

1. **Look**
   ▶ Look at the teacher as the word is said.

2. **Listen**
   ▶ Listen carefully.

3. **Write**
   ▶ Write the word clearly with a pencil.

4. **Check**
   ▶ Check your spelling.

My Learning
GOAL
I will spell _____ words correctly on my unit test.

My Learning
PLAN
What will I do this week to learn my spelling words?

I'll do it.   I did it.
☐ **Big Activity** ☐

Practice Unit ⑪

Tuesday

My Learning Goal is the number of words you want to spell correctly on your unit test. Write your goal here.

Tuesday

My Learning Plan helps you decide what you'll do to learn your spelling words.

A **Week** With *Spell It—Write!*

Wednesday

To practice your words, do the activities on your learning plan. Make the **Big Activity** part of your plan.

Word Box

job   leg   nut   set   bad

BIG ACTIVITY!

Read each group of words below. Then write the word from the Word Box that rhymes with the words in each group.

1. pet, net, met _____

2. but, cut, hut _____

3. Bob, rob, mob _____

4. sad, lad, had _____

5. Meg, Peg, beg _____

12 Practice Unit

Spelling and writing go together. **Write It Right** helps you practice your writing.

Friday

Your unit test will cover all the words you studied.

 Pick something on this list. Pretend you are planning to do what you pick. Write a list of things you need to do to get ready.
- give a birthday party
- go to a baseball game
- take a trip with your family
- plant a garden

your ideas with a partner.

Thursday

Are you ready? helps you decide whether you are ready for your unit test.

 Are you ready?
To find out, take a self-test or take a practice test with a partner.

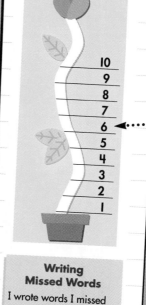

GOAL

I spelled _____ words correctly on my unit test.

10
9
8
7
6
5
4
3
2
1

Writing Missed Words
I wrote words I missed in **My Word Journal**.

☐

Practice Unit ⑬

Friday

Graph your score on the unit test here.

Friday

Write words you missed in **My Word Journal** so you remember to study them later. Then check the box.

MY WORD LIST

job

leg

nut

set

bad

Getting to Know *Spell It—Write!*

Sentences

1. My mother has a new **job**.

2. This old teddy bear has only one **leg**.

3. We watched the squirrel hide a **nut**.

4. Would you please **set** the table?

5. It's too **bad** the library is closed.

Are my words spelled right?

BIG IDEA!

I can help myself learn to spell with *Spell It—Write!*

Taking Your Spelling Test

1 **Look**
▶ Look at the teacher as the word is said.

2 **Listen**
▶ Listen carefully.

3 **Write**
▶ Write the word clearly with a pencil.

4 **Check**
▶ Check your spelling.

My Learning PLAN

What will I do this week to learn my spelling words?

I'll do it.		I did it.
☐	**Big Activity**	☐

job   leg   nut   set   bad

BIG ACTIVITY!

Read each group of words below. Then write the word from the Word Box that rhymes with the words in each group.

1. pet, net, met   _____

2. but, cut, hut   _____

3. Bob, rob, mob   _____

4. sad, lad, had   _____

5. Meg, Peg, beg   _____

Write It Right

Pick something on this list. Pretend you are planning to do what you pick. Write a list of things you need to do to get ready.

- give a birthday party
- go to a baseball game
- take a trip with your family
- plant a garden

Share your ideas with a partner.

Are you ready?
To find out, take a self-test or take a practice test with a partner.

Meeting My GOAL

I spelled _____ words correctly on my unit test.

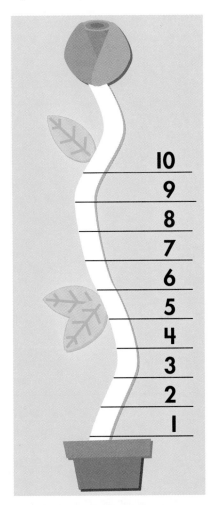

10
9
8
7
6
5
4
3
2
1

Writing Missed Words

I wrote words I missed in **My Word Journal**.

☐

MY WORD LIST

wish

help

went

down

wet

zoo

miss

rest

Spelling Is Important

Sentences

1. I **wish** the rain would stop.

2. I'll **help** you lift the box.

3. Ann **went** to the park.

4. My sled flew **down** the hill.

5. The dog shook its **wet** fur.

6. We saw lions and tigers at the **zoo**.

7. Did you **miss** the bus?

8. Cindy ate the **rest** of the grapes.

Are my words spelled right?

BIG IDEA!

Correct spelling helps others read what you write.

Did You Know...?

Some words—like **rest**—have more than one meaning. For example, you know that you can rest when you are tired. You can also eat the rest of your dinner. What other words do you know that have more than one meaning?

I will spell _____ words correctly on my unit test.

What will I do this week to learn my spelling words?

I'll do it.		I did it.
☐	**Big Activity**	☐
☐	**Flip Folder**	☐

Helper Pages (pp. 169–175) have more information.

BIG ACTIVITY!

It's your turn to be the teacher! One word in each group is spelled right. Circle it. Write the correct word on the line. Use the Word Box to check your spelling.

1 wet   wett   whet   _____

2 help   hlep   hilp   _____

3 wint   whent   went   _____

4 whish   wish   wich   _____

5 zu   zoo   zoe   _____

6 down   doun   don   _____

7 resst   rest   rist   _____

8 miss   mis   micc   _____

Draw a line through any words that you think are not spelled right. Write the correct spelling above each word. Check your spelling.

Dear Kim,

I wennt to the zu today. I wsh you

had been there, too! The man dwnn

by the seals let me hilpp feed one. He

fed the rst of them. I got all wt, too!

See you later,

Scott

Are you ready?
To find out, take a self-test or take a practice test with a partner.

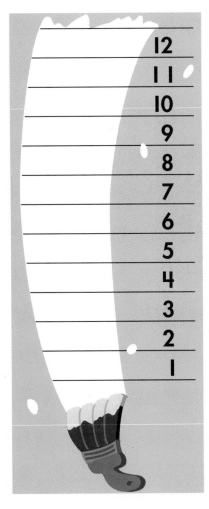

I spelled _____ words correctly on my unit test.

12
11
10
9
8
7
6
5
4
3
2
1

Writing Missed Words

I wrote words I missed in **My Word Journal**.

☐

MY WORD LIST

land

men

fix

king

grass

next

bat

inch

Short Vowels: a, e, i

Sentences

1. I watched the airplane **land**.

2. Six **men** ran in the race.

3. I can **fix** my own lunch.

4. The **king** sits on a gold chair.

5. Mom cut the **grass**.

6. My grandma will visit us **next** week.

7. Bobby hit the ball with his lucky **bat**.

8. This bug is one **inch** long.

Are my words spelled right?

BIG IDEA!

- Listen to the vowel sound in **land**. It is called **short a** and is spelled with an **a**.
- Listen to the vowel sound in **men**. It is called **short e** and is spelled with an **e**.
- Listen to the vowel sound in **fix**. It is called **short i** and is spelled with an **i**.

Study Tip

1 **Look** at the word.

Say the word.

2 **Cover** the word.

See the word in your mind.

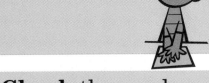

3 **Write** the word.

Check the word.

My Learning GOAL

I will spell _____ words correctly on my unit test.

My Learning PLAN

What will I do this week to learn my spelling words?

I'll do it.		I did it.
☐	**Big Activity**	☐
☐	**Flip Folder**	☐

Helper Pages (pp. 169–175) have more information.

BIG ACTIVITY!

- Take turns reading the words in the Word Box out loud with a partner.
- Write Word Box words with a **short a** sound under the hat. Write words with a **short e** sound under the net and words with a **short i** sound under the fish.

Work with a partner.
- Use words on your spelling list to make up story titles.
- Draw a star by the title you like the best.

Are you ready?
To find out, take a self-test or take a practice test with a partner.

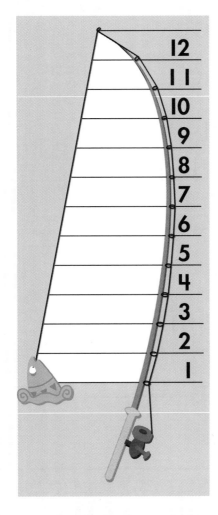

I spelled _____ words correctly on my unit test.

12
11
10
9
8
7
6
5
4
3
2
1

Writing Missed Words

I wrote words I missed in **My Word Journal**.

MY WORD LIST

fox

bus

lot

jump

doll

cut

drop

cup

_____

_____

_____

_____

_____

Short Vowels: o, u

Sentences

1. The **fox** has a bushy tail.

2. I ride a **bus** to school.

3. We saw a **lot** of clowns at the circus.

4. My dog can **jump** over a fence.

5. Molly made a green dress for her **doll**.

6. Kevin **cut** a circle from the yellow paper.

7. A **drop** of rain fell on my nose.

8. The **cup** is full of milk.

Are my words spelled right?

BIG IDEA!

- Listen to the vowel sound in **fox**. It is called **short o** and is spelled with an **o**.
- Listen to the vowel sound in **bus**. It is called **short u** and is spelled with a **u**.

Did You Know…?

Anyone can ride a bus to get where they need to go. Our word **bus** is short for a much older word, **omnibus**. **Omnibus** meant "wagon for everyone."

My Learning GOAL

I will spell _____ words correctly on my unit test.

My Learning PLAN

What will I do this week to learn my spelling words?

I'll do it.		I did it.
☐	**Big Activity**	☐
☐	**Flip Folder**	☐
☐	**Spelling Tic-Tac-Toe**	☐

Helper Pages (pp. 169–175) have more information.

fox	bus	cut	jump
doll	lot	drop	cup

BIG ACTIVITY!

- Take turns reading the words in the Word Box out loud with a partner.
- Write Word Box words with a **short o** sound under the stop sign. Write words with a **short u** sound under the sun.

Think about all the ways people can travel.

- Write your list here.
- Circle the ways you have used.
- On a piece of paper, write about your favorite way to travel. Why is it your favorite?

I spelled _____ words correctly on my unit test.

| 12 |
| 11 |
| 10 |
| 9 |
| 8 |
| 7 |
| 6 |
| 5 |
| 4 |
| 3 |
| 2 |
| 1 |

Writing Missed Words

I wrote words I missed in **My Word Journal**.

Are you ready?

To find out, take a self-test or take a practice test with a partner.

MY WORD LIST

hold

tell

best

fold

keep

call

hill

gold

Spelling Tip

Sentences

1. I'll **hold** your skates for you.

2. Shall I **tell** you a story?

3. We like the outdoor games **best**.

4. Please **fold** your paper down the middle.

5. Can you **keep** a secret?

6. Kiki will **call** you about the party.

7. We ran to the top of the **hill**.

8. My grandfather wears a **gold** ring.

Are my words spelled right?

BIG IDEA!

If you're not sure how to spell a word, think of a word that rhymes. The last parts of rhyming words are often spelled the same.

Check Your Spelling

When you copy words, check your spelling.

1 **Copy** one letter at a time.

2 **Check** each letter.

   Check the whole word.

3 **Ask** your teacher if you need help.

I will spell _____ words correctly on my unit test.

My Learning PLAN

What will I do this week to learn my spelling words?

I'll do it.		I did it.
☐	**Big Activity**	☐
☐	**Flip Folder**	☐
☐	**Spelling Tic-Tac-Toe**	☐

Helper Pages (pp. 169–175) have more information.

BIG ACTIVITY!

Each underlined word below rhymes with a word in the Word Box. Write a rhyming word from the Word Box to finish each sentence.

1 Please _____ me when you hear the <u>bell</u>.

2 There may be _____ in that <u>old</u> cave.

3 Will you help me _____ this <u>old</u> blanket?

4 The farmer wants to _____ the biggest <u>sheep</u>.

5 This is the _____ grade I ever had on a <u>test</u>.

6 You can _____ your mother from the <u>mall</u>.

7 Jack and <u>Jill</u> went up the _____.

8 Dad <u>told</u> me to _____ my sister's hand.

Write it Right

What words do you know that rhyme with **tell**?

- Write your list here.
- Mark the parts of the words that are spelled the same.

_____

_____

_____

_____

_____

_____

_____

_____

_____

_____

_____

Are you ready?

To find out, take a self-test or take a practice test with a partner.

I spelled _____ words correctly on my unit test.

| 12 |
| 11 |
| 10 |
| 9 |
| 8 |
| 7 |
| 6 |
| 5 |
| 4 |
| 3 |
| 2 |
| 1 |

Writing Missed Words

I wrote words I missed in **My Word Journal**. ☐

MY WORD LIST

mad

made

have

bath

grade

hand

take

add

game

ask

gave

ate

Short a, Long a

Sentences

1. My grandma never gets **mad**.

2. Look at the mask I **made**!

3. Do you **have** a blue crayon?

4. The **bath** water is too hot!

5. We are in second **grade**.

6. Derek writes with his left **hand**.

7. Dad will **take** the baby to the park.

8. I can **add** big numbers.

9. Our **game** begins at two o'clock.

10. **Ask** the teacher to help us.

11. Mrs. Miller **gave** me this book.

12. We **ate** lunch outside today.

Are my words spelled right?

BIG IDEA!

- Listen to **mad**. The **short a** sound is spelled **a**.
- Listen to **made**. The **long a** sound is spelled **a**-consonant-**silent e**.

Word Sort

 **Look** at the word.    **Say** the word.

2 **Use** the sounds you hear and the spelling patterns you see to match the word with other words like it.

3 **Put** words that don't fit under the question mark (**?**).

MY Learning GOAL

I will spell _____ words correctly on my unit test.

MY Learning PLAN

What will I do this week to learn my spelling words?

I'll do it.		I did it.
☐	**Word Sort Sheet**	☐
☐	**Big Activity**	☐
☐	**Flip Folder**	☐
☐	**Spelling Tic-Tac-Toe**	☐

Helper Pages (pp. 169–175) have more information.

mad   made   have   grade   bath   hand
take   add   game   gave   ask   ate

BIG ACTIVITY!

- Take turns reading the words in the Word Box out loud with your partner.
- Write each Word Box word under the **Master Word** with the same sound and spelling pattern.
- If a word doesn't fit, write it under the **?**.

Master Word m**a**d	Master Word m**a**de	**?**

Work with a partner.
- Make a list of things to take on a trip to the beach.
- Pick one of these things. Write about it. Tell why you would take it with you.

Are you ready?
To find out, take a self-test or take a practice test with a partner.

I spelled _____ words correctly on my unit test.

12
11
10
9
8
7
6
5
4
3
2
1

Writing Missed Words

I wrote words I missed in **My Word Journal**.

My Word List

base

nail

lay

baby

cake

away

late

pay

rain

today

paid

way

Long a

Sentences

1. John slid into second **base**.

2. Mom used a **nail** to hang the picture.

3. **Lay** the wet paintings on the table.

4. Mrs. Lopez has a new **baby**.

5. What kind of **cake** do you like?

6. Please put the games **away**.

7. Hurry, or we'll be **late**!

8. How much did you **pay** for lunch?

9. The **rain** sounds like music.

10. Do we have art class **today**?

11. Mrs. Adams **paid** me to walk her dog.

12. Which **way** should I go?

Are my words spelled right?

BIG IDEA!

- Listen to **base**. The **long a** sound in this word is spelled **a**-consonant-**silent e**.
- Listen to **nail**. The **long a** sound is spelled **ai**.
- Listen to **lay**. The **long a** sound is spelled **ay**.

My Learning GOAL

I will spell _____ words correctly on my unit test.

Word Sort

1 **Look** at the word.   **Say** the word.

2 **Use** the spelling patterns you see to match the word with other words like it.

3 **Put** words that don't fit under the question mark (**?**).

My Learning PLAN

What will I do this week to learn my spelling words?

I'll do it.		I did it.
☐	**Word Sort Sheet**	☐
☐	**Big Activity**	☐
☐	**Flip Folder**	☐
☐	**Spelling Tic-Tac-Toe**	☐

Helper Pages (pp. 169–175) have more information.

base	nail	lay	away	cake	baby
late	rain	pay	today	paid	way

BIG ACTIVITY!

- Take turns reading the words in the Word Box with your partner.
- Write each Word Box word under the **Master Word** with the same spelling pattern.
- If a word doesn't fit, write it under the **?**.

Master Word base	Master Word nail	Master Word lay	?

Write It Right

What do you need to make a cake?
- Write a list of what you need.
- Write sentences telling what you would do first, second, and third to make the cake.

Are you ready?
To find out, take a self-test or take a practice test with a partner.

Meeting My GOAL

I spelled _____ words correctly on my unit test.

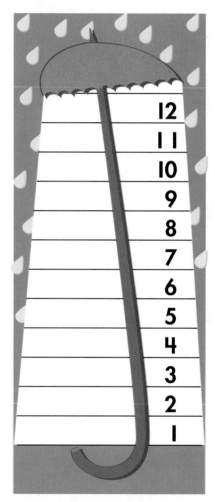

12
11
10
9
8
7
6
5
4
3
2
1

Writing Missed Words

I wrote words I missed in **My Word Journal**.

☐

MY WORD LIST

met

seen

end

tree

egg

seem

when

sleep

Short e, Long e

Sentences

1. I **met** Marta at the swimming pool.

2. Have you **seen** my coat?

3. How does the story **end**?

4. The apple **tree** has pretty flowers.

5. There is a crack in this **egg**.

6. Mike does not **seem** happy today.

7. **When** does summer begin?

8. Where do ducks **sleep**?

Are my words spelled right?

BIG IDEA!

- Listen to **met**. The **short e** sound is spelled **e**.
- Listen to **seen**. The **long e** sound is spelled **ee**.

Did You Know...?

Baby birds come from eggs. The word **egg** comes from an old word meaning "bird."

My Learning GOAL

I will spell _____ words correctly on my unit test.

My Learning PLAN

What will I do this week to learn my spelling words?

I'll do it.		I did it.
☐	**Big Activity**	☐
☐	**Flip Folder**	☐
☐	**Spelling Tic-Tac-Toe**	☐

Helper Pages (pp. 169–175) have more information.

Word Box

met	seen	end	tree
egg	seem	when	sleep

BIG ACTIVITY!

Write a word from the Word Box to finish each sentence.

1 How would you like me to cook your _____?

2 _____ is your birthday?

3 Carla and Sam _____ last year.

4 The last person is at the _____ of the line.

5 Have you ever _____ a rainbow before?

6 There is a big pine _____ in our yard.

7 The children _____ happy while they are playing.

8 Do you _____ eight hours every night?

Work with a partner.
- Make a list of words that tell about trees.
- Use the words to write about a tree.

Are you ready?
To find out, take a self-test or take a practice test with a partner.

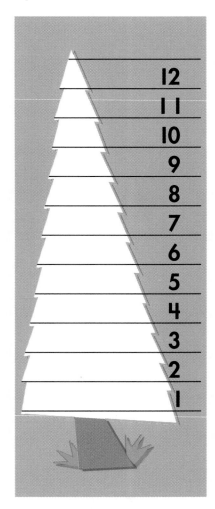

I spelled _____ words correctly on my unit test.

| 12 |
| 11 |
| 10 |
| 9 |
| 8 |
| 7 |
| 6 |
| 5 |
| 4 |
| 3 |
| 2 |
| 1 |

Writing Missed Words

I wrote words I missed in **My Word Journal**.

Long e

My Word List

need

clean

happy

any

cheek

read

sheet

eat

Sentences

1. Does David **need** a pencil?

2. We will **clean** our desks today.

3. I was **happy** when we won the game.

4. Robby does not have **any** clay.

5. Ann has blue paint on her **cheek**.

6. Ms. West likes to **read** stories to us.

7. I have one **sheet** of paper left.

8. We **eat** lunch at noon.

Are my words spelled right?

BIG IDEA!

- Listen to **need**. The **long e** sound in this word is spelled **ee**.
- Listen to **clean**. The **long e** sound is spelled **ea**.
- Listen to **happy**. The **long e** sound is spelled **y**.

Did You Know...?

We get the word **happy** from the old word **hap**. A hap was luck, or a chance for something good to happen. Now when we say we are happy, we mean we are glad.

GOAL

I will spell _____ words correctly on my unit test.

PLAN

What will I do this week to learn my spelling words?

I'll do it.		I did it.
☐	**Big Activity**	☐
☐	**Flip Folder**	☐
☐	**Spelling Tic-Tac-Toe**	☐

Helper Pages (pp. 169–175) have more information.

Word Box

need   sheet   happy   any
cheek   read   clean   eat

BIG ACTIVITY!

Use a different word from the Word Box to answer each rhyming riddle.

1 I always make you nice and neat,
So wash your hands before you eat. _____

2 End my spelling with a **d**.
I have two **e**'s. Can you find me? _____

3 I'm the soft part of your face.
I get red when you run a race. _____

4 I'm a cover on your bed.
You pull me over your head. _____

5 My **long e** sound is spelled with **y**.
If you feel like this, you won't cry! _____

6 I'm what you do when you open a book,
So check one out and take a look. _____

7 I'm a word that rhymes with **penny,**
But my spelling looks more like **many**. _____

8 My **long e** sound is spelled **ea**.
You do this with food three times a day. _____

Write It Right

What would you take on a long walk? Write your list here.

Are you ready?
To find out, take a self-test or take a practice test with a partner.

I spelled _____ words correctly on my unit test.

12
11
10
9
8
7
6
5
4
3
2
1

Writing Missed Words

I wrote words I missed in **My Word Journal**.

☐

MY WORD LIST

store
been
more
buy
your
wind
were
fall

Using a Dictionary

Sentences

1. Dad went to the **store** for milk.

2. We have **been** playing all day.

3. Do you need **more** glue?

4. I want to **buy** a toy for Suzy.

5. Is this **your** lunch box?

6. The **wind** blew away Tanya's hat.

7. We **were** at the baseball game.

8. The trees are pretty in the **fall**.

Are my words spelled right?

BIG IDEA!

A dictionary can help you spell words. Words in a dictionary are arranged in A-B-C order.

Did You Know...?

Some words have more than one meaning. The first meaning of **store** was "a good supply." Later, it meant "to put away." The newest meaning of **store** is "a place to buy things." Today, we use all three meanings of this word!

1841

GRAFTON VILLAGE STORE

My Learning GOAL

I will spell _____ words correctly on my unit test.

My Learning PLAN

What will I do this week to learn my spelling words?

I'll do it.		I did it.
☐	**Big Activity**	☐
☐	**Flip Folder**	☐
☐	**Spelling Tic-Tac-Toe**	☐

Helper Pages (pp. 169–175) have more information.

Word Box

| store | been | more | buy |
| your | wind | fall | were |

BIG ACTIVITY!

This is Tina's spelling dictionary. Help Tina add words to her dictionary in A-B-C order. Write each word from the Word Box where it belongs.

add

bat

_____

_____

bus

_____

_____

cup

doll

egg

_____

_____

grass

hill

inch

jump

keep

land

_____

_____

need

paid

rain

_____

_____

tell

very

_____

_____

_____

_____

zoo

Work with a partner to think of things you can find out from a dictionary. Write them here.

I spelled _____ words correctly on my unit test.

| 12 |
| 11 |
| 10 |
| 9 |
| 8 |
| 7 |
| 6 |
| 5 |
| 4 |
| 3 |
| 2 |
| 1 |

WHAT CAN YOU FIND INSIDE ME?

Dictionary

Writing Missed Words

I wrote words I missed in **My Word Journal**.

☐

Are you ready?
To find out, take a self-test or take a practice test with a partner.

MY WORD LIST

bit

bite

nice

hid

mile

line

hide

five

Short i, Long i

Sentences

1. The puppy **bit** my finger.

2. Sam took a **bite** of the apple.

3. Mr. Jackson is a **nice** teacher.

4. Dad **hid** my birthday present.

5. Rita lives one **mile** from school.

6. Linda is the first one in **line**.

7. I'll **hide** behind the chair.

8. My cat is **five** years old.

Are my words spelled right?

BIG IDEA!

- Listen to **bit**. The **short i** sound is spelled **i**.
- Listen to **bite**. The **long i** sound is spelled **i**-consonant-**silent e**.

Rhyme and Spell

1 If you don't know how to spell a word, think of a word that rhymes.

2 The last parts of rhyming words are often spelled the same.

My Learning PLAN

What will I do this week to learn my spelling words?

I'll do it.		I did it.
☐	**Big Activity**	☐
☐	**Flip Folder**	☐
☐	**Spelling Tic-Tac-Toe**	☐

Helper Pages (pp. 169–175) have more information.

BIG ACTIVITY!

Read each word in the Word Box. Decide if it has a **short i** sound or a **long i** sound. Write each word in the correct list. Then circle the **silent e** at the end of **long i** words.

Short i Words

Long i Words

Work with a partner.

- Think of things you might find in a big, dark cave.
- Write a list.
- Use your list to write about what is in the cave.

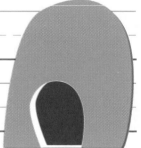

Are you ready?
To find out, take a self-test or take a practice test with a partner.

I spelled _____ words correctly on my unit test.

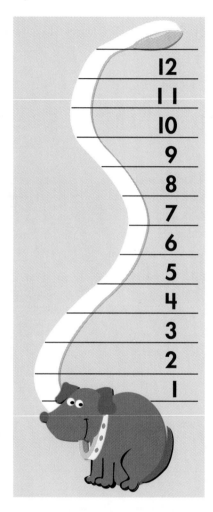

12
11
10
9
8
7
6
5
4
3
2
1

Writing Missed Words

I wrote words I missed in **My Word Journal**.

☐

MY WORD LIST

fine

sky

night

try

ice

fly

light

why

Long i

Sentences

1. We had a **fine** time at the zoo.

2. There were four jets in the **sky**.

3. Did you hear the rain last **night**?

4. Will you **try** to jump rope?

5. I saw **ice** on the pond today.

6. The baby bird is learning to **fly**.

7. Please turn off the **light**.

8. **Why** is grass green?

Are my words spelled right?

BIG IDEA!

- Listen to **fine**. The **long i** sound is spelled **i**-consonant-**silent e**.
- Listen to **sky**. The **long i** sound is spelled **y**.
- Listen to **night**. The **long i** sound is spelled **igh**.

Did You Know…?

Is a **knight** the same as a **night**? Words that sound the same but have different meanings and spellings are called **homophones**. **Knight** and **night** are homophones. How are the meanings different?

GOAL

I will spell _____ words correctly on my unit test.

PLAN

What will I do this week to learn my spelling words?

I'll do it.		I did it.
☐	**Big Activity**	☐
☐	**Flip Folder**	☐
☐	**Spelling Tic-Tac-Toe**	☐

Helper Pages (pp. 169–175) have more information.

BIG ACTIVITY!

Match each clue to a word in the Word Box. Write the word in the boxes. When you finish, look for a message in the circled letters. Use the message to finish the sentence at the bottom.

1 I mean "very good."

2 Look up to see me.

3 A bird can, a butterfly can, but you can't!

4 You can see the sun in the morning and the moon at _____.

5 If it's not dark, it's _____.

6 I am very cold!

7 I start a lot of questions.

8 Can you do it? You'll never know unless you _____.

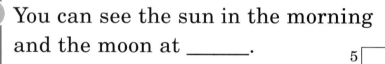

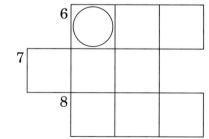

All the words have a _____ sound.

Many questions begin with the word **why**.

- Think of some questions you want to ask that start with **why**.
- Write your questions here.
- Work with a partner or by yourself to find the answer to one of your questions.

Are you ready?

To find out, take a self-test or take a practice test with a partner.

I spelled _____ words correctly on my unit test.

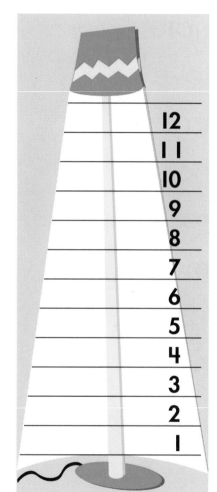

12
11
10
9
8
7
6
5
4
3
2
1

Writing Missed Words

I wrote words I missed in **My Word Journal**.

☐

Short o, Long o

MY WORD LIST

not

note

love

trot

hop

rose

mop

woke

nose

joke

hope

glove

Sentences

1. I do **not** like peas.

2. The teacher wrote a **note** on my paper.

3. Grandpa's letter said, "I **love** you."

4. Rosa trained her horse to **trot**.

5. Can you **hop** on one foot?

6. Jane put a pink **rose** in the vase.

7. Slip! Slop! Get the **mop**!

8. Pat **woke** up at seven o'clock.

9. The monkey has a funny **nose**.

10. Mary told a **joke** about a chicken.

11. I **hope** you can come over today.

12. I cannot find my other **glove**.

Are my words spelled right?

BIG IDEA!

- Listen to **not**. The **short o** sound is spelled **o**.
- Listen to **note**. The **long o** sound is spelled **o**-consonant-**silent e**.

Word Sort

1 **Look** at the word. **Say** the word.

2 **Use** the sounds you hear and the spelling patterns you see to match the word with other words like it.

3 **Put** words that don't fit under the question mark (**?**).

I will spell _____ words correctly on my unit test.

My Learning **PLAN**

What will I do this week to learn my spelling words?

I'll do it.		I did it.
☐	**Word Sort Sheet**	☐
☐	**Big Activity**	☐
☐	**Flip Folder**	☐
☐	**Spelling Tic-Tac-Toe**	☐

Helper Pages (pp. 169–175) have more information.

| not | note | love | trot | hop | rose |
| mop | woke | nose | joke | hope | glove |

BIG ACTIVITY!

- Take turns reading the words in the Word Box out loud with your partner.
- Write each Word Box word under the **Master Word** with the same sound and spelling pattern.
- If a word doesn't fit, write it under the **?**.

Master Word n<u>o</u>t	Master Word n<u>o</u>te	?

- On the first line, write the name of a person who would like to get a note from you.
- Write your note.
- Check your note for spelling mistakes and fix them.
- Copy the note in your best writing. Sign your name at the end of the note. Then mail it.

Dear _____,

I spelled _____ words correctly on my unit test.

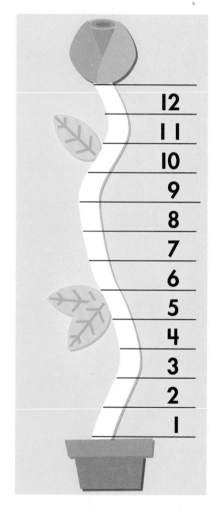

12
11
10
9
8
7
6
5
4
3
2
1

Writing Missed Words

I wrote words I missed in **My Word Journal**.

☐

Are you ready?

To find out, take a self-test or take a practice test with a partner.

My Word List

cone

boat

show

cold

ago

coat

pole

most

grow

road

hose

row

Long o

Sentences

1. Would you like an ice cream **cone**?

2. Six people can ride in this **boat**.

3. Diane can **show** you the way.

4. It is **cold** and rainy today.

5. My grandmother was born long **ago**.

6. Will I need my **coat** today?

7. We need another **pole** for our tent.

8. Which team has the **most** points?

9. How tall does corn **grow**?

10. Ron lives on this **road**.

11. Dan used a **hose** to water the garden.

12. Is my seat in this **row**?

Are my words spelled right?

BIG IDEA!

- Listen to **cone**. The **long o** sound is spelled **o**-consonant-**silent e**.
- Listen to **boat**. The **long o** sound is spelled **oa**.
- Listen to **show**. The **long o** sound is spelled **ow**.

Word Sort

① **Look** at the word.   **Say** the word.

② **Use** the spelling patterns to match the word with other words like it.

③ **Put** words that don't fit under the question mark (**?**).

Word Box

cone	boat	show	cold	ago	coat
pole	most	grow	road	hose	row

BIG ACTIVITY!

- Take turns reading the words in the Word Box with your partner.
- Write each Word Box word under the **Master Word** with the same spelling pattern.
- If a word doesn't fit, write it under the **?**.

Master Word <u>cone</u>	Master Word sh<u>ow</u>	Master Word b<u>oat</u>	?

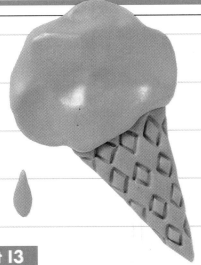

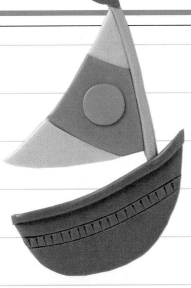

Work with a partner to make a list of people you might see in a circus. Write the list here.

Are you ready?
To find out, take a self-test or take a practice test with a partner.

I spelled _____ words correctly on my unit test.

12
11
10
9
8
7
6
5
4
3
2
1

Writing Missed Words

I wrote words I missed in **My Word Journal**.

☐

MY WORD LIST

who

saw

want

off

myself

how

fell

what

Proofreading

Sentences

1. **Who** is at the door?

2. We **saw** a rainbow in the sky.

3. I **want** to finish this book.

4. Did you turn **off** the light?

5. I can do this puzzle **myself**.

6. **How** did you get here so fast?

7. Two inches of snow **fell** last night.

8. **What** is your name?

Are my words spelled right?

BIG IDEA!

Proofread to check your writing.

Proofread It!

1 Read each sentence.

2 Is it clear?
▶ Does the sentence make sense?
▶ Can others read your handwriting?

3 Note errors.
▶ Are the words spelled right?

who   saw   want   off
myself   how   fell   what

BIG ACTIVITY!

Help Carla proofread her writing. Cross out the misspelled word in each sentence. Write the correct spelling on the line.

1. Jack fel down. _____

2. I can fix it mysellf. _____

3. I get of the bus here. _____

4. Howe much are two and two? _____

5. Do you wannt to read this book? _____

6. I saww a funny show on TV. _____

7. Hoo sits next to you? _____

8. Wut did you buy at the store? _____

Check Lila's note for spelling. Cross out words that are spelled wrong. Write the correct word above the mistake. Rewrite Lila's note on another piece of paper.

Dear Tanya,

Hou are you? I whant to tell you hoo I saww. I saw Carrie! Do you know wat she did? She fel of her bike. I'm glad she was not hurt. Later, I went to the park by my self.

Please write to me soon.

Your friend,

Lila

Are you ready?
To find out, take a self-test or take a practice test with a partner.

Meeting My GOAL

I spelled _____ words correctly on my unit test.

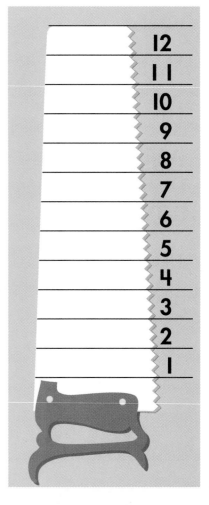

12
11
10
9
8
7
6
5
4
3
2
1

Writing Missed Words
I wrote words I missed in **My Word Journal**.

☐

MY WORD LIST

little

many

after

put

house

some

give

very

Words Writers Use

Sentences

1. I need a **little** more glue on this paper.

2. How **many** girls are in your class?

3. I'll meet you **after** school.

4. Tad **put** his papers in his desk.

5. Nina lives in the blue **house**.

6. Do you need **some** help?

7. We can **give** you a ride to school.

8. This book is **very** interesting.

Are my words spelled right?

BIG IDEA!

It's important to know how to spell words we use often when we write.

Be a Word Hunter!

1 **Look** around you for words you want to learn to spell.

2 **Write** the words in **My Word Journal**.

3 **Make** sure you only write words you don't know how to spell.

My Learning GOAL

I will spell _____ words correctly on my unit test.

My Learning PLAN

What will I do this week to learn my spelling words?

I'll do it.		I did it.
☐	**Big Activity**	☐
☐	**Flip Folder**	☐
☐	**Spelling Tic-Tac-Toe**	☐

Helper Pages (pp. 169–175) have more information.

little	many	after	put
house	some	give	very

BIG ACTIVITY!

The famous author, Phil A. Page, is speaking to your class. Here is his speech. Cross out his mistakes and write the words correctly at the bottom of the page.

Thank you vary much for inviting me to your class. I have written miny books. I know that spelling is important. I will giv you som ideas that work. First, I find a quiet spot in the howse so I can think. I always check my words aftir I have finished writing and fix my mistakes. If I putt a littel extra time into checking my spelling, I am happy with my work!

_____

_____

_____

_____

- Choose one picture on this page. Write about how the picture looks, but do not say what it is.
- Ask a partner to read your writing and guess which picture you wrote about.

I spelled _____ words correctly on my unit test.

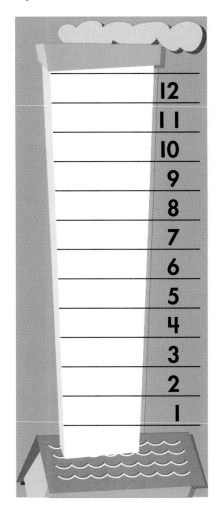

12
11
10
9
8
7
6
5
4
3
2
1

Writing Missed Words

I wrote words I missed in **My Word Journal**.

Are you ready?

To find out, take a self-test or take a practice test with a partner.

MY WORD LIST

say

stay

slow

pot

low

spot

start

snow

s Blends

Sentences

1. What did you **say**?

2. Let's **stay** here until Dad comes.

3. Please **slow** down.

4. The soup in the **pot** is ready to eat.

5. The children sat on **low** chairs.

6. Jean has a **spot** on her shirt.

7. The bike race will **start** at noon.

8. It is starting to **snow**.

Are my words spelled right?

Be a Word Hunter!

BIG IDEA!

- Consonants work alone or in blends. Listen to **say**. The **s** works alone.
- Listen to **stay**. The **s** and **t** work together.

Check Your Spelling

1 **Copy** one letter at a time.

2 **Check** each letter.

3 **Check** the whole word.

What will I do this week to learn my spelling words?

I'll do it.		I did it.
☐	**Big Activity**	☐
☐	**Flip Folder**	☐
☐	**Spelling Tic-Tac-Toe**	☐

Helper Pages (pp. 169–175) have more information.

BIG ACTIVITY!

Some of the letters fell off the signs below. Use the words in the Word Box to decide which letters are missing. Write the words on the lines below.

STORE HOURS
8:00am to 10:00pm
__tart early
and __tay late

__ow,
low
prices

Don't be
__low,
shop today

__now Shovels
$10.00

__ot $5.00

__ay it with
Flowers

_____ _____ _____

_____ _____ _____

Which Word Box word was not used?   _____
Write that word here.   _____

Write It Right

What do you know about snow? Think about what it looks like, how it feels, and what you can do in it. Write everything you know here.

Are you ready?
To find out, take a self-test or take a practice test with a partner.

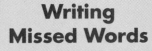
Be a Word Hunter!

I spelled _____ words correctly on my unit test.

| 12 |
| 11 |
| 10 |
| 9 |
| 8 |
| 7 |
| 6 |
| 5 |
| 4 |
| 3 |
| 2 |
| 1 |

Writing Missed Words

I wrote words I missed in **My Word Journal**. ☐

MY WORD LIST

black

club

flag

glad

play

plant

clap

glass

l Blends

Sentences

1. We named our **black** cat Inky.

2. We have a reading **club** at school.

3. The **flag** is blowing in the wind.

4. I'm **glad** you are in my class.

5. We can **play** softball after lunch.

6. Who will water this **plant** for me?

7. Let's **clap** for the winners!

8. Would you like a **glass** of milk?

Are my words spelled right?

Be a Word Hunter!

BIG IDEA!

Remember that consonants can work together in blends. Listen to **black, club, flag, glad,** and **play**. The consonant blends in these words are **bl, cl, fl, gl,** and **pl**.

My Learning GOAL

I built **My Word List**. ☐

I checked my words for correct spelling. ☐

I will spell _____ words correctly on my unit test.

Study Tip

1 **Look** at the word.

Say the word.

2 **Cover** the word.

See the word in your mind.

3 **Write** the word.

Check your spelling.

My Learning PLAN

What will I do this week to learn my spelling words?

I'll do it.		I did it.
☐	**Big Activity**	☐
☐	**Flip Folder**	☐
☐	**Spelling Tic-Tac-Toe**	☐
☐	**Speller's Workouts**	☐

Helper Pages (pp. 169–175) have more information.

BIG ACTIVITY!

Write letters in the blanks to make a word in the Word Box. Then write the whole word.

1 ___ – ___ – a – c – k   _____

2 ___ – ___ – a – p   _____

3 ___ – ___ – u – b   _____

4 ___ – a – s – s   _____

5 ___ – a – d   _____

6 ___ – ___ – a – g   _____

7 ___ – ___ – a – y   _____

8 ___ – ___ – a – n – t   _____

Use this space to draw a picture of one of your spelling words. Then write about your picture. Proofread your writing.

I spelled _____ words correctly on my unit test.

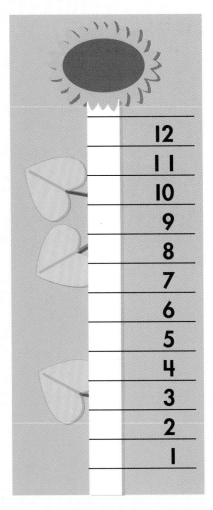

| 12 |
| 11 |
| 10 |
| 9 |
| 8 |
| 7 |
| 6 |
| 5 |
| 4 |
| 3 |
| 2 |
| 1 |

Writing Missed Words

I wrote words I missed in **My Word Journal**.

Be a Word Hunter!

Are you ready?
To find out, take a self-test or take a practice test with a partner.

MY WORD LIST

bring

dress

frog

green

crack

brush

train

drive

r Blends

Sentences

1. Please **bring** the book to me.

2. Alice wore a blue **dress** to the party.

3. Tammy has a pet **frog**.

4. I will draw **green** leaves on the tree.

5. There is a **crack** in the window.

6. I **brush** my teeth three times a day.

7. I can hear a **train** coming.

8. Can your mom **drive** us to the store?

Are my words spelled right?

Be a Word Hunter!

BIG IDEA!

Listen to **bring, dress, frog,** and **green**. The consonant blends in these words are **br, dr, fr,** and **gr**.

Did You Know...?

The English word for **frog** has been almost the same for hundreds of years! First our name for this little green animal was spelled **frogge,** then **froge**. Do you think **frog** is easier to spell?

My Learning GOAL

I built **My Word List**. ☐

I checked my words for correct spelling. ☐

I will spell _____ words correctly on my unit test.

My Learning PLAN

What will I do this week to learn my spelling words?

I'll do it.		I did it.
☐	**Big Activity**	☐
☐	**Flip Folder**	☐
☐	**Spelling Tic-Tac-Toe**	☐
☐	**Speller's Workouts**	☐

Helper Pages (pp. 169–175) have more information.

Word Box

green   dress   bring   frog
crack   brush   train   drive

BIG ACTIVITY!

Draw a line through the word in each sentence that is wrong. Write the correct word.

1. I found a big creen frog in a pond on my vacation. _____

2. I put it in a pocket of my fress. _____

3. I had my drush in the other pocket. _____

4. I wanted to dring the frog home. _____

5. I knew the frog wouldn't mind the long crive in the car. _____

6. But Mom said we had to take a drain home instead. _____

7. So I put the brog in a big jar to carry it back to the pond. _____

8. I dropped the jar and it got a big brack! The frog hopped back to the pond. _____

Write It Right

Work with a partner to make a list of things that are green. Write your list here. Can the things on your list grow, or get bigger? Circle the ones that can grow.

Are you ready?
To find out, take a self-test or take a practice test with a partner.

Be a
Word Hunter!

Meeting My GOAL

I spelled ________ words correctly on my unit test.

12
11
10
9
8
7
6
5
4
3
2
1

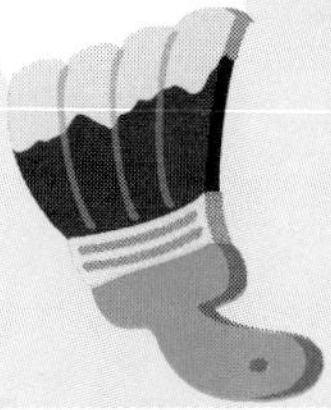

Writing Missed Words

I wrote words I missed in **My Word Journal**. ☐

ar, or

park

corn

story

far

horse

hard

part

north

Sentences

1. Let's meet at the **park** after school.

2. My aunt grows **corn** on her farm.

3. Mr. Washington read a **story** to us.

4. Is your family moving **far** away?

5. I rode a **horse** at the fair.

6. This clay is too **hard** to use.

7. Would you like **part** of this apple?

8. I live **north** of the school.

Be a Word Hunter!

Are my words spelled right?

BIG IDEA!

- Listen to **park**. The vowel sound is made by **a** and **r** working together.
- Listen to **corn**. The vowel sound is made by **o** and **r** working together.

Be a Word Hunter!

1. **Look** around you for words you want to learn to spell.

2. **Write** the words in **My Word Journal**.

3. **Make** sure you only write words you don't know how to spell.

BIG ACTIVITY!

Read each word in the Word Box. Write each word spelled with **ar** under the shark. Write each word spelled with **or** under the sea horse. Draw a line under the letters **ar** and **or** in each word.

Work with a partner to make a list of things you might see on a walk in a park. Write your list here. Use your list to write a paragraph about your walk in the park. Proofread your writing.

Welcome to the Park

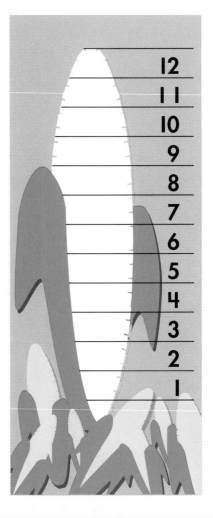

I spelled _____ words correctly on my unit test.

12
11
10
9
8
7
6
5
4
3
2
1

Writing Missed Words

I wrote words I missed in **My Word Journal**.

Be a Word Hunter!

Are you ready?
To find out, take a self-test or take a practice test with a partner.

MY WORD LIST

from

first

form

three

farm

born

girl

there

r With Vowels

Sentences

1. Marty got a letter **from** her brother.

2. Carol was the **first** player to score.

3. Please write your name on this **form**.

4. Don's sister is **three** years old.

5. Cows and pigs live on the **farm**.

6. These kittens were **born** last week.

7. There is a new **girl** in our class.

8. We'll put the table over **there**.

Are my words spelled right?

Be a Word Hunter!

BIG IDEA!

- Listen to **from**. The **r** comes before the vowel.
- Listen to **first**. The **r** comes after the vowel.
- Listen carefully to words with **r** to hear if the **r** comes before or after the vowel.

Proofread It!

1 Read each sentence.

2 Is it clear?
▶ Does the sentence make sense?
▶ Can others read your handwriting?

3 Note errors.
▶ Are the words spelled right?

My Learning GOAL

I built
My Word List. ☐

I checked my words for correct spelling. ☐

I will spell _____ words correctly on my unit test.

My Learning PLAN

What will I do this week to learn my spelling words?

I'll do it.		I did it.
☐	**Big Activity**	☐
☐	**Flip Folder**	☐
☐	**Spelling Tic-Tac-Toe**	☐
☐	**Speller's Workouts**	☐

Helper Pages (pp. 169–175) have more information.

BIG ACTIVITY!

Use each pair of words in the Word Box to finish one of the sentences below. Then read the sentences aloud to be sure they make sense. Use the Word Box to check your spelling.

1 A new calf was _____ on the _____ .

2 _____ are _____ apples in the bowl.

3 This _____ won _____ prize.

4 You can get a _____ _____ your teacher.

Work with a partner.
- Make a list of animals that live on a farm. Write your list here.
- Choose one animal. Write about how it looks and sounds. You might want to draw a picture.
- Proofread your writing.

I spelled _____ words correctly on my unit test.

12
11
10
9
8
7
6
5
4
3
2
1

Writing Missed Words
I wrote words I missed in **My Word Journal**.

□

Be a Word Hunter!

Are you ready?
To find out, take a self-test or take a practice test with a partner.

MY WORD LIST

bike

duck

milk

took

talk

work

rock

wake

back

make

truck

sick

k Sound: k, ck

Sentences

1. Do you ride your **bike** to school?

2. We fed a **duck** at the pond.

3. I would like some **milk,** please.

4. Dad **took** us to the zoo today.

5. My baby sister can **talk**.

6. Mom goes to **work** at eight o'clock.

7. Jerry threw a **rock** into the lake.

8. Loud noises will **wake** the baby.

9. When will Mr. Gomez be **back**?

10. I can **make** a castle in the sand.

11. Grandpa's **truck** is bright red.

12. Linda was **sick** on Monday.

Are my words spelled right?

Be a Word Hunter!

BIG IDEA!

The **k** sound at the end of a word is usually spelled with **k,** as in **bike, milk,** and **took,** or **ck,** as in **duck**.

Word Sort

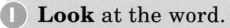
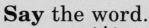

① **Look** at the word.   **Say** the word.

② **Use** the spelling patterns you see to match the word with other words like it.

③ **Put** words that don't fit under the question mark (**?**).

BIG ACTIVITY!

- Take turns reading the words in the Word Box with your partner.
- Write each Word Box word under the **Master Word** with the same spelling pattern.

Master Word b**ike**	Master Word mil**k**	Master Word du**ck**	Master Word too**k**

Write it Right

Make a list of things you might bring to a sick friend. Write your list here.

Get Well

Are you ready?
To find out, take a self-test or take a practice test with a partner.

Be a Word Hunter!

I spelled _____ words correctly on my unit test.

12
11
10
9
8
7
6
5
4
3
2
1

Writing Missed Words

I wrote words I missed in **My Word Journal**.

MY WORD LIST

child

ship

much

fish

each

wash

shoe

reach

ch, sh

Sentences

1. My dad was once a **child** like me.

2. Have you ever sailed on a **ship**?

3. There is too **much** milk in my cup.

4. I counted twenty **fish** in the tank.

5. Please give a book to **each** person.

6. **Wash** your hands before you eat.

7. Anthony lost his **shoe** during the race.

8. How high can you **reach**?

Are my words spelled right?

Be a Word Hunter!

BIG IDEA!

- Listen to **child** and **much**. The sound at the start of **child** and the end of **much** is spelled **ch**.
- Listen to **ship** and **fish**. The sound at the start of **ship** and the end of **fish** is spelled **sh**.

Did You Know...?

You know that a shoe is something you put on your foot. Did you know that horses also wear shoes? What kind of shoes do horses wear? Horses wear horseshoes, of course!

My Learning **GOAL**

I built
My Word List. ☐

I checked my words for correct spelling. ☐

I will spell _____ words correctly on my unit test.

My Learning **PLAN**

What will I do this week to learn my spelling words?

I'll do it.		I did it.
☐	**Big Activity**	☐
☐	**Flip Folder**	☐
☐	**Spelling Tic-Tac-Toe**	☐
☐	**Speller's Workouts**	☐

Helper Pages (pp. 169–175) have more information.

Word Box

each	shoe	much	fish
child	wash	reach	ship

BIG ACTIVITY!

Use a pair of words from the Word Box to finish each sentence. Decide which words make the most sense.

1. Those muddy sneakers should go to a _____ _____ _____.

2. The shelf is _____ too high to _____.

3. My father is a sailor on a _____ _____.

4. _____ _____ has a can of paint.

Work with a partner to make a list of things you know about fish. Write your list here.

I spelled _____ words correctly on my unit test.

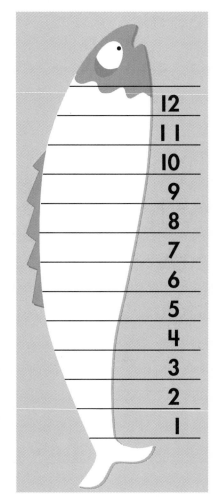

12
11
10
9
8
7
6
5
4
3
2
1

Be a Word Hunter!

Are you ready?
To find out, take a self-test or take a practice test with a partner.

Writing Missed Words

I wrote words I missed in **My Word Journal**. ☐

My Word List

them

thank

these

other

than

both

they

that

th

Sentences

1. May I go with **them** to the park?

2. **Thank** you for the presents!

3. Do you like **these** pink shoes?

4. Robert ate the **other** apple.

5. Your book is bigger **than** mine.

6. We can **both** play this game.

7. **They** will visit us after lunch.

8. Please give **that** book to Lee.

Are my words spelled right?

Be a Word Hunter!

Unit 23

BIG IDEA!

- Listen to **them**. The sound at the start of **them** is spelled **th**.
- Listen to **thank**. The sound at the start of **thank** is also spelled **th**.

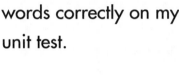

Study Tip

1 **Look** at the word.   **Say** the word.

2 **Cover** the word.   **See** the word in your mind.

3 **Write** the word.   **Check** your spelling.

My Learning GOAL

I built **My Word List**. ☐

I checked my words for correct spelling. ☐

I will spell _____ words correctly on my unit test.

My Learning PLAN

What will I do this week to learn my spelling words?

I'll do it.		I did it.
☐	**Big Activity**	☐
☐	**Flip Folder**	☐
☐	**Spelling Tic-Tac-Toe**	☐
☐	**Speller's Workouts**	☐

Helper Pages (pp. 169–175) have more information.

BIG ACTIVITY!

Read each sentence. Write the word from the Word Box that best fits the meaning of the sentence. Then go back and circle the **th** in each word.

1 Did you see _____ big red balloon?

2 I am taller _____ you.

3 _____ jeans are new.

4 Why are _____ singing a song now?

5 Did you _____ her for helping you?

6 We sent _____ some flowers.

7 Mother gave _____ of us a pear.

8 Where is your _____ mitten?

Work with a partner to make a list of things that might be in this box. Write your list here.

I spelled _____ words correctly on my unit test.

12
11
10
9
8
7
6
5
4
3
2
1

Be a Word Hunter!

Are you ready?
To find out, take a self-test or take a practice test with a partner.

Writing Missed Words

I wrote words I missed in **My Word Journal**.

☐

Family Names

sister
father
uncle
daddy
mother
aunt
mommy
brother

Sentences

1. Sara is my only **sister**.

2. Dan's **father** is our soccer coach.

3. Lee's **uncle** always tells jokes.

4. I call my father "**daddy**."

5. My **mother** works downtown.

6. Does your **aunt** live nearby?

7. The baby wants her **mommy**.

8. Do you have a **brother**?

Are my words spelled right?

Be a Word Hunter!

BIG IDEA!

People in families have special names for the roles they play. Knowing how to spell these names will help you when you write about your family.

Test Yourself

Do this for every word on your spelling list.

1. **Look** at the word.

2. **Cover** the word.   **Write** the word.

3. **Correct** your self-test. Write the correct spelling next to any word you did not spell right.

I built **My Word List**. ☐

I checked my words for correct spelling. ☐

I will spell _____ words correctly on my unit test.

My Learning PLAN

What will I do this week to learn my spelling words?

I'll do it.		I did it.
☐	**Big Activity**	☐
☐	**Flip Folder**	☐
☐	**Spelling Tic-Tac-Toe**	☐
☐	**Speller's Workouts**	☐

Helper Pages (pp. 169–175) have more information.

BIG ACTIVITY!

Use the words in the Word Box to do the puzzle.

Across

1. She is married to your uncle.

4. Another name for daddy

6. A baby's name for mother

7. He has the same parents as you.

8. She might be your twin.

Down

2. He is your mom's brother.

3. You might call your father this.

5. Parents are a father and a _____.

Write the name of each person in your family. Don't forget to write your name, too! Next to each name, write things that person likes to do.

I spelled _____ words correctly on my unit test.

| 12 |
| 11 |
| 10 |
| 9 |
| 8 |
| 7 |
| 6 |
| 5 |
| 4 |
| 3 |
| 2 |
| 1 |

**Writing
Missed Words**

I wrote words I missed in **My Word Journal**.

☐

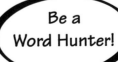
Be a
Word Hunter!

Are you ready?
To find out, take a self-test or take a practice test with a partner.

How Am

Read each question. Circle your answer.
Talk about your answers with your teacher.

Do I hunt words every week?
   Yes   Most of the time   No

Do I hunt words I can learn to spell?
   Yes   Most of the time   No

GOAL

Do I use the *Study Tip* and tips on taking tests to help me?
   Yes
   Most of the time
   No

Do I meet my spelling goals?
   Yes
   Most of the time
   No

My Learning PLAN

Does my learning plan help me learn my words?
   Yes   Most of the time   No

Do I take self-tests or practice tests to see if I know my spelling words?
   Yes   Most of the time   No

How Am I Doing?

Write it Right

Do I check my spelling when I write?

Yes　　　Most of the time　　　No

Notes From My Teacher:

Finish the sentence. Share your answer with a partner.

I am making progress as a speller because

MY WORD LIST

Endings: -ed

My Word List

looked
played
needed
bent
wanted
asked
planted
walked
told
helped
called
rained

Sentences

1. Maria **looked** out the window.
2. We **played** baseball all afternoon.
3. Jan **needed** new shoes.
4. The trees **bent** low in the wind.
5. The baby **wanted** his father.
6. She **asked** me to come to the party.
7. Our class **planted** flowers.
8. Mrs. Fong **walked** her dog today.
9. Carlos **told** a funny story.
10. Mrs. Garcia **helped** me with math.
11. I **called** Grandpa on his birthday.
12. It **rained** all day on Sunday.

Are my words spelled right?

Be a Word Hunter!

BIG IDEA!

- Listen to **looked**. The ending is spelled **-ed**.
- Listen to **played**. The ending is spelled **-ed**.
- Listen to **needed**. The ending is spelled **-ed**.

Word Sort

① **Look** at the word. **Say** the word.

 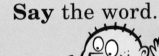

② **Use** the sounds you hear and the letter patterns you see to match the word with other words like it.

③ **Put** words that don't fit under the question mark (**?**).

I built **My Word List**. ☐

I checked my words for correct spelling. ☐

I will spell _____ words correctly on my unit test.

My Learning PLAN

What will I do this week to learn my spelling words?

I'll do it.		I did it.
☐	**Word Sort Sheet**	☐
☐	**Big Activity**	☐
☐	**Flip Folder**	☐
☐	**Spelling Tic-Tac-Toe**	☐
☐	**Speller's Workouts**	☐

Helper Pages (pp. 169–175) have more information.

looked   needed   bent   wanted   called   asked
planted   walked   told   helped   played   rained

BIG ACTIVITY!

- Take turns reading the words in the Word Box with your partner.
- Write each Word Box word under the **Master Word** with the same sound and spelling pattern.
- If a word doesn't fit, write it under the **?**.

Master Word looked	Master Word played	Master Word needed	?

Write it Right

What day was yesterday?
- Write the day in the center.
- Write what happened to you yesterday on the lines.
- Choose one thing and write about it on a separate piece of paper.

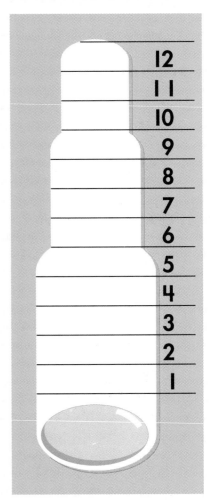

I spelled _____ words correctly on my unit test.

12
11
10
9
8
7
6
5
4
3
2
1

Writing Missed Words

I wrote words I missed in **My Word Journal**.

☐

Are you ready?

To find out, take a self-test or take a practice test with a partner.

Be a Word Hunter!

MY WORD LIST

boats

birds

wishes

inches

houses

dresses

boxes

horses

Plurals: -s, -es

Sentences

1. Tom likes to make toy **boats**.

2. Do you hear the **birds** singing?

3. Do your **wishes** come true?

4. There are 12 **inches** in a foot.

5. I counted all the white **houses** I saw.

6. Kim got two new **dresses**.

7. Please put the books in the **boxes**.

8. My grandmother owns three **horses**.

Are my words spelled right?

Be a Word Hunter!

BIG IDEA!

- Listen to **boats** and **birds**. The plural ending in these words is spelled **-s**.
- Listen to **wishes** and **inches**. The plural ending in these words is spelled **-es**.

My Learning GOAL

I built **My Word List**. ☐

I checked my words for correct spelling. ☐

I will spell _____ words correctly on my unit test.

My Learning PLAN

What will I do this week to learn my spelling words?

I'll do it.		I did it.
☐	**Big Activity**	☐
☐	**Flip Folder**	☐
☐	**Spelling Tic-Tac-Toe**	☐
☐	**Speller's Workouts**	☐
☐	**My Own Activity**	☐

Helper Pages (pp. 169–175) have more information.

Did You Know...?

Do boxes grow on trees? Long ago, people made the first boxes with wood from the box tree. Our word **box** comes from the name of this tree.

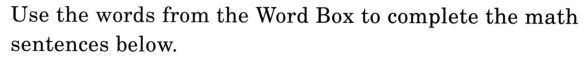

Word Box

boats   birds   wishes   inches
houses   dresses   boxes   horses

BIG ACTIVITY!

Use the words from the Word Box to complete the math sentences below.

1. 1 bird + 1 bird = 2 _____

2. 1 box + 1 box = 2 _____

3. 1 dress + 1 dress = 2 _____

4. 1 wish + 1 wish = 2 _____

5. 1 boat + 1 boat = 2 _____

6. 1 horse + 1 horse = 2 _____

7. 1 inch + 1 inch = 2 _____

8. 1 house + 1 house = 2 _____

 **Write it Right**

Work with a partner to make a list of words about boats. Make another list about birds. Circle the words that could be on both lists.

Boats   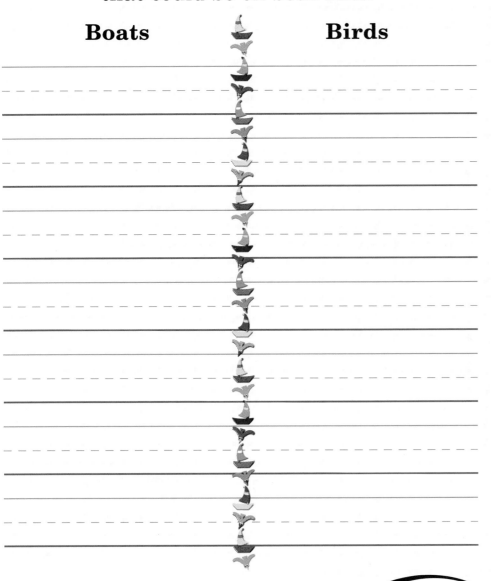   **Birds**

 **Are you ready?**
To find out, take a self-test or take a practice test with a partner.

I spelled _____ words correctly on my unit test.

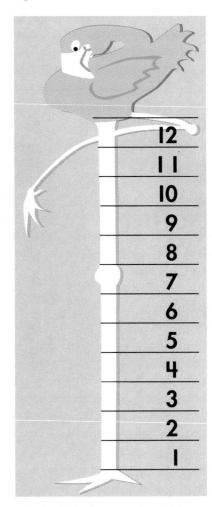

12
11
10
9
8
7
6
5
4
3
2
1

Writing Missed Words

I wrote words I missed in **My Word Journal**.

☐

MY WORD LIST

said

goes

walk

now

know

going

has

dear

Spelling Tip

Sentences

1. Dad **said** I can go with you.

2. Our class **goes** to the school library every Friday.

3. I'll take the puppy for a **walk**.

4. Anthony has to go home **now**.

5. I **know** all my spelling words.

6. Are you **going** to the party?

7. Susan **has** a new kitten.

8. Oh, **dear,** I forgot my mittens.

Are my words spelled right?

Be a Word Hunter!

BIG IDEA!

If you're not sure how to spell a word, write it out. Check to see if your spelling is correct.

Rhyme and Spell

1 If you don't know how to spell a word, think of a word that rhymes.

2 The last parts of rhyming words are often spelled the same.

walk, talk

My Learning PLAN

What will I do this week to learn my spelling words?

I'll do it.   I did it.
☐ **Big Activity** ☐
☐ **Flip Folder** ☐
☐ **Spelling Tic-Tac-Toe** ☐
☐ **Speller's Workouts** ☐
☐ **My Own Activity** ☐

Helper Pages (pp. 169–175) have more information.

Word Box

said	goes	walk	now
know	going	has	dear

BIG ACTIVITY!

One word in each sentence is written three different ways.
Circle the word you think is right and write the word on
the line. Use the Word Box to check your spelling.

1. My bike [has, hass, haz] a red horn. _____

2. She said, "Oh, [dear, dere, daer]!" _____

3. We can [wawk, wak, walk] to the park. _____

4. It's time to go to bed [noww, nou, now]. _____

5. He [goes, goz, gose] to the farm every year. _____

6. I don't [now, know, no] where my hat is. _____

7. Where are you [gowing, goong, going]? _____

8. She [sed, said, sead], "Open your books." _____

122   Unit 27

Think about people that you might write a letter to. Write their names on the lines. Then write your letter on a separate piece of paper.

I spelled _____ words correctly on my unit test.

People

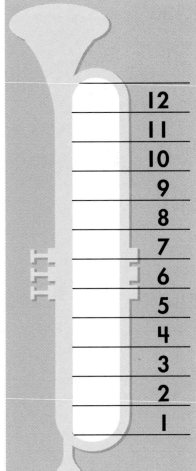

12
11
10
9
8
7
6
5
4
3
2
1

Start your letter like this: Dear _____ ,

Be a Word Hunter!

Writing Missed Words

I wrote words I missed in **My Word Journal**.

☐

Are you ready?
To find out, take a self-test or take a practice test with a partner.

MY WORD LIST

tall

kiss

fill

moss

full

still

wall

pull

_____

_____

_____

_____

_____

_____

Final Consonants: ll, ss

Sentences

1. How **tall** are you?

2. Dad always gives me a goodnight **kiss**.

3. Please **fill** this can with red paint.

4. There is **moss** growing on this tree.

5. This box is **full** of old toys.

6. Are you **still** playing that game?

7. We have one more **wall** to paint.

8. I'll **pull** you in the wagon.

Are my words spelled right?

Be a Word Hunter!

BIG IDEA!

- Listen to **tall**. The last sound in the word **tall** is spelled **ll**.
- Listen to **kiss**. The last sound in the word **kiss** is spelled **ss**.

Did You Know...?

A kiss on the cheek shows love in many countries. The words for **kiss** often look and sound alike in other languages, too. In Sweden, the word is **kyssa,** in Denmark it is **kysse,** and in Germany it is **kussen**. What is the same about each of the spellings?

I built **My Word List**. ☐

I checked my words for correct spelling. ☐

I will spell _____ words correctly on my unit test.

My Learning PLAN

What will I do this week to learn my spelling words?

I'll do it.		I did it.
☐	**Big Activity**	☐
☐	**Flip Folder**	☐
☐	**Spelling Tic-Tac-Toe**	☐
☐	**Speller's Workouts**	☐
☐	**My Own Activity**	☐

Helper Pages (pp. 169–175) have more information.

BIG ACTIVITY!

Use a word from the Word Box to complete each rhyme. Write the word on the line.

1 Mama says that she will miss me.
She can't wait to hug and _____ me.

_____

2 My big brother's not short at all.
He seems like he's ten feet _____.

_____

3 I made this picture of the trees in fall.
See—I hung it on my _____.

_____

4 In the forest, you may walk across
some green, brown, or golden _____.

_____

5 I just talked to my brother, Bill.
He says it's too cold to swim—_____!

_____

6 John said he would pull the wagon for us,
But he can't because it's too _____ of us.

_____

7 The sun will make my painting fade.
Would you please _____ down the shade?

_____

8 A little more, but please don't _____ it.
If it's too full, I might spill it!

_____

Look around your classroom. What is hanging on the walls? What hangs on your walls at home? Make two lists here. Choose one thing and write about it.

Things on the Walls at School	Things on the Walls at Home

Be a Word Hunter!

Are you ready?
To find out, take a self-test or take a practice test with a partner.

I spelled _____ words correctly on my unit test.

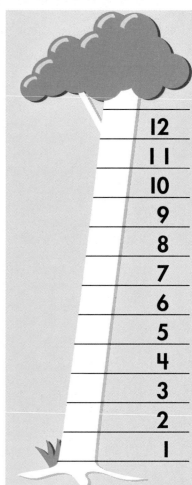

12
11
10
9
8
7
6
5
4
3
2
1

Writing Missed Words
I wrote words I missed in **My Word Journal**.
☐

MY WORD LIST

started
hoped
hopped
liked
loved
named
saved
patted
tapped
hummed
hugged
stayed

Endings: -ed

Sentences

1. The concert **started** late.

2. Dana **hoped** for good weather today.

3. The rabbit **hopped** into the bushes.

4. I think Tia **liked** the necklace I made.

5. I **loved** the movie we saw last night!

6. Have you **named** your new puppy yet?

7. We **saved** our cans for recycling.

8. I **patted** the puppy's head lightly.

9. Mom **tapped** Jill on the shoulder.

10. We **hummed** the words we didn't know.

11. My brother **hugged** his stuffed bear.

12. We **stayed** at school to wait for Dad.

Are my words spelled right?

Be a Word Hunter!

BIG IDEA!

- When you add **-ed** to a word that ends in **silent e,** drop the **e** and add **-ed: hope, hoped**.

- When you add **-ed** to a word that ends with one vowel and one consonant, double the consonant and add **-ed: hop, hopped**.

Word Sort

① **Look** at the word.   **Say** the word.

② **Use** the sounds you hear and the letter patterns you see to match the word with other words like it.

My Learning GOAL

I built **My Word List**. ☐

I checked my words for correct spelling. ☐

I will spell _____ words correctly on my unit test.

My Learning PLAN

What will I do this week to learn my spelling words?

I'll do it.		I did it.
☐	**Word Sort Sheet**	☐
☐	**Big Activity**	☐
☐	**Flip Folder**	☐
☐	**Spelling Tic-Tac-Toe**	☐
☐	**Speller's Workouts**	☐
☐	**My Own Activity**	☐

Helper Pages (pp. 169–175) have more information.

started   hoped   hummed   saved   hopped   liked
tapped   named   hugged   stayed   loved   patted

BIG ACTIVITY!

- Take turns reading the words in the Word Box with your partner.
- Write each Word Box word under the **Master Word** with the same spelling pattern.

Master Word **hop<u>ed</u>**	**Master Word** **hopp<u>ed</u>**	**Master Word** **start<u>ed</u>**

Write It Right

What do you think the boy in the picture is reading about? Make a list of words that might tell about the story in his book. Write your list here.

A Dinosaur Named Bill

Are you ready?
To find out, take a self-test or take a practice test with a partner.

Be a Word Hunter!

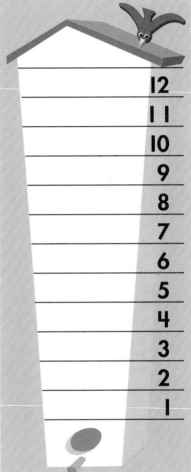

I spelled _____ words correctly on my unit test.

12
11
10
9
8
7
6
5
4
3
2
1

Writing Missed Words

I wrote words I missed in **My Word Journal**.

☐

MY WORD LIST

Endings: -ing

Sentences

eating

hoping

hopping

waving

giving

making

coming

putting

doing

sitting

riding

running

1. We'll be **eating** at six o'clock.

2. Juan is **hoping** for a sunny day.

3. We saw rabbits **hopping** in the park.

4. The flag is **waving** in the wind.

5. Mrs. Franklin is **giving** a test.

6. Uncle Jim is **making** our lunch.

7. Aunt Jo is **coming** on the bus.

8. I am **putting** my toys away.

9. What are you **doing** on Saturday?

10. We were **sitting** on the floor.

11. I was **riding** my bike on the path.

12. Are you **running** in the race?

Be a Word Hunter!

Are my words spelled right?

BIG IDEA!

- When you add **-ing** to a word that ends in **silent e,** drop the **e** and add **-ing: hope, hoping**.
- When you add **-ing** to a word that ends with one vowel and one consonant, double the consonant and add **-ing: hop, hopping**.

Word Sort

1 **Look** at the word. **Say** the word.

 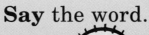

2 **Use** the sounds you hear and the letter patterns you see to match the word with other words like it.

Word Box

putting hoping doing sitting hopping waving
making coming eating giving running riding

BIG ACTIVITY!

- Take turns reading the words in the Word Box with your partner.
- Write each Word Box word under the **Master Word** with the same spelling pattern.

Master Word hop**ping**	Master Word hop**ing**	Master Word eat**ing**

Write It Right

What do you like to do on Saturday?
Write your list here.

_____

Are you ready?
To find out, take a self-test
or take a practice test with
a partner.

Be a
Word Hunter!

Meeting My GOAL

I spelled _____
words correctly on
my unit test.

| 12 |
| 11 |
| 10 |
| 9 |
| 8 |
| 7 |
| 6 |
| 5 |
| 4 |
| 3 |
| 2 |
| 1 |

**Writing
Missed Words**

I wrote words I missed
in **My Word Journal**.

☐

MY WORD LIST

doghouse

inside

raincoat

outside

baseball

bluebird

playpen

sailboat

Compound Words

Sentences

1. Sara painted the **doghouse**.

2. Please go **inside** before it rains.

3. Grandma wore a yellow **raincoat**.

4. We went **outside** after lunch.

5. Mario threw the **baseball** to me.

6. A **bluebird** lives in our tree.

7. Dad put the baby in the **playpen**.

8. We saw a **sailboat** at the lake.

Are my words spelled right?

Be a Word Hunter!

BIG IDEA!

Listen to **doghouse**. **Dog** and **house** make **doghouse**. **Doghouse** is a compound word because it is made by putting two words together.

Study Tip

① **Look** at the word.

Say the word.

② **Cover** the word.

See the word in your mind.

③ **Write** the word.

Check your spelling.

My Learning GOAL

I built **My Word List**. ☐

I checked my words for correct spelling. ☐

I will spell _____ words correctly on my unit test.

My Learning PLAN

What will I do this week to learn my spelling words?

I'll do it.		I did it.
☐	**Big Activity**	☐
☐	**Flip Folder**	☐
☐	**Spelling Tic-Tac-Toe**	☐
☐	**Speller's Workouts**	☐
☐	**My Own Activity**	☐

Helper Pages (pp. 169–175) have more information.

BIG ACTIVITY!

Use words from the Word Box to do this crossword puzzle.

Across

3. Not inside

5. It's played with a bat and ball.

7. A home for a pet

8. Something to wear so you won't get wet

Down

1. An animal with wings

2. It floats on water and you can ride in it.

4. Not outside

6. A safe place for a baby

Choose one picture on this page. Describe it here. Then ask a partner to read what you wrote and guess which picture you wrote about.

I spelled _____ words correctly on my unit test.

12
11
10
9
8
7
6
5
4
3
2
1

Be a Word Hunter!

Writing Missed Words

I wrote words I missed in **My Word Journal**.

Are you ready?
To find out, take a self-test or take a practice test with a partner.

MY WORD LIST

hear

here

hour

our

are

to

too

two

Homophones

Sentences

1. Robert can **hear** the music.

2. Suki asked us to meet her **here**.

3. The show starts in one **hour**.

4. **Our** team won the game.

5. These apples **are** for your family.

6. We'll go **to** the store after school.

7. We had **too** many people for one team.

8. My sister is **two** years old.

Are my words spelled right?

Be a Word Hunter!

BIG IDEA!

Words that sound alike but are spelled differently are called **homophones**. You need to know the spelling that goes with the meaning you want.

Did You Know...?

How many minutes are in one hour? The word **hour** comes from a very old word that meant "season." Much later, **hour** came to mean "sixty minutes." Would you like to count the number of minutes in a whole summer?

My Learning GOAL

I built **My Word List**. ☐

I checked my words for correct spelling. ☐

I will spell _____ words correctly on my unit test.

My Learning PLAN

What will I do this week to learn my spelling words?

I'll do it.		I did it.
☐	**Big Activity**	☐
☐	**Flip Folder**	☐
☐	**Spelling Tic-Tac-Toe**	☐
☐	**Speller's Workouts**	☐
☐	**My Own Activity**	☐

Helper Pages (pp. 169–175) have more information.

BIG ACTIVITY!

Write the correct homophone to finish each sentence.

Word Box

to   too   two

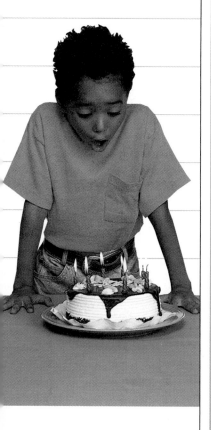

Happy birthday _____ you!

There are _____ shoes in a pair.

My brother is _____ little for school.

Word Box

are   hour   our

This is _____ house.

Tony and Shane _____ on the bus.

One _____ is the same as 60 minutes.

Word Box

hear   here

Can you _____ the music?

We can play ball _____ .

**Write it Right**

Work with a partner to think of things you can count by twos. Write your list here.

I spelled _____ words correctly on my unit test.

	12
	11
	10
	9
	8
	7
	6
	5
	4
	3
	2
	1

Writing Missed Words

I wrote words I missed in **My Word Journal**.

☐

Are you ready?
To find out, take a self-test or take a practice test with a partner.

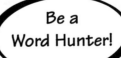Be a Word Hunter!

How Am

Do I hunt words every week?
Yes   Most of the time   No

Do I hunt words I can learn to spell?
Yes   Most of the time   No

Do I use the *Study Tip* and tips on taking tests to help me?
Yes
Most of the time
No

Do I meet my spelling goals?
Yes
Most of the time
No

Does my learning plan help me learn my words?
Yes   Most of the time   No

Do I take self-tests or practice tests to see if I know my spelling words?
Yes   Most of the time   No

I Doing?

Do I check my spelling when I write?

Yes   Most of the time   No

Finish the sentence. Share your answer with a partner.

I am making progress as a speller because

My Word Journal is only for words you do not know how to spell. Write new words you want to learn to spell. You can also write words you have misspelled in your writing or on a unit spelling test.

Choose words from **My Word Journal** to add to your weekly word lists. When you write a word on your weekly list, draw a circle around it in **My Word Journal**. When you spell the word correctly on your unit test, cross it out in **My Word Journal**.

If you don't spell the word correctly, write it on another weekly list later.

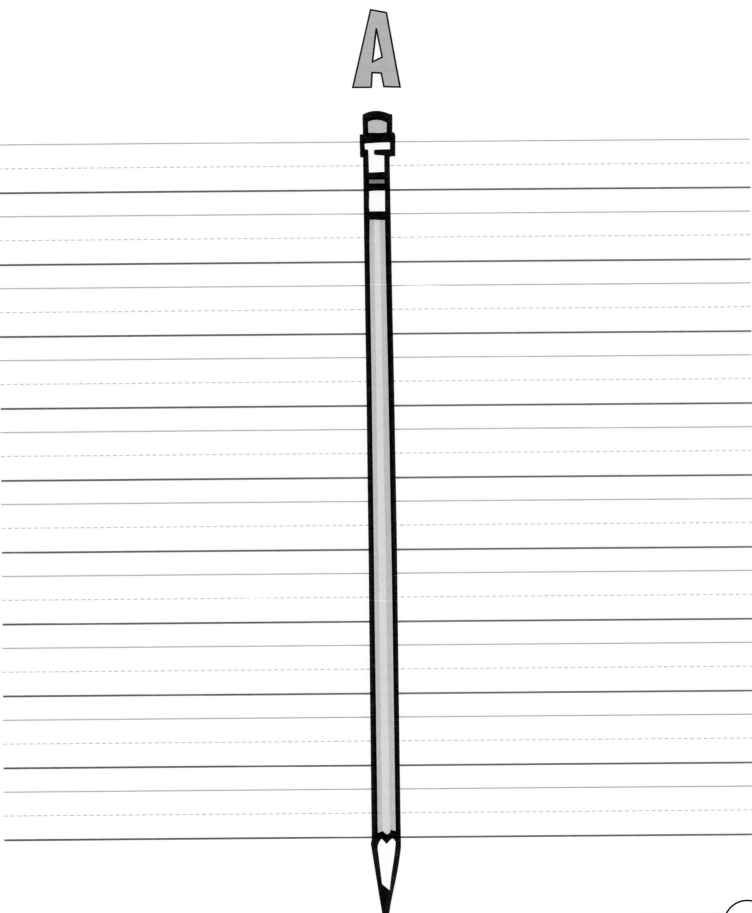

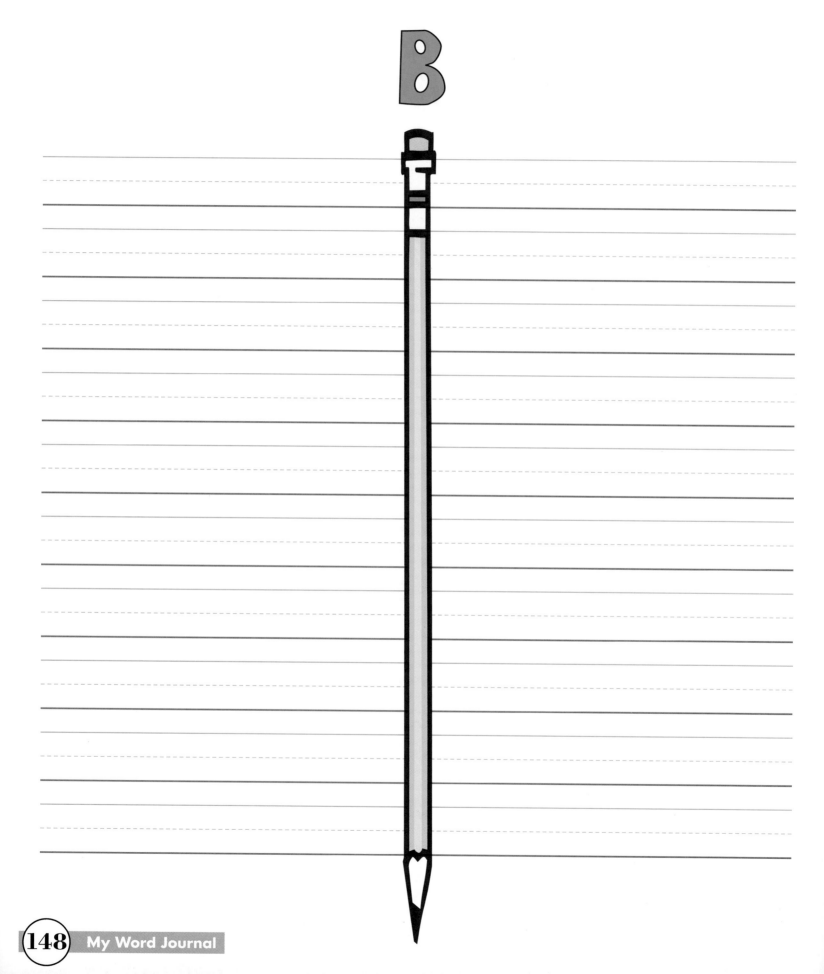

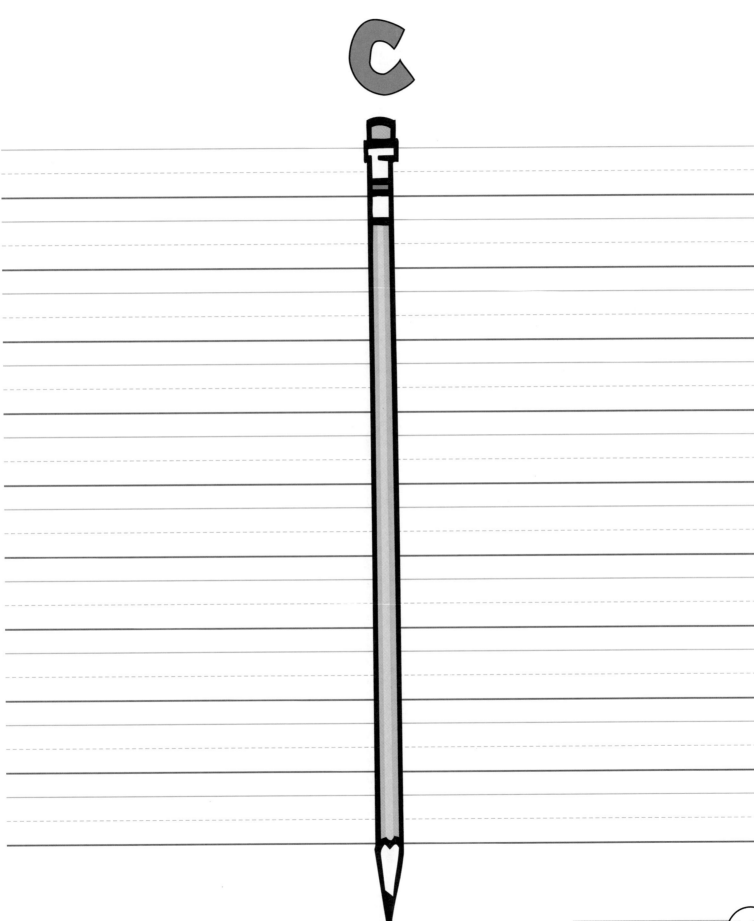

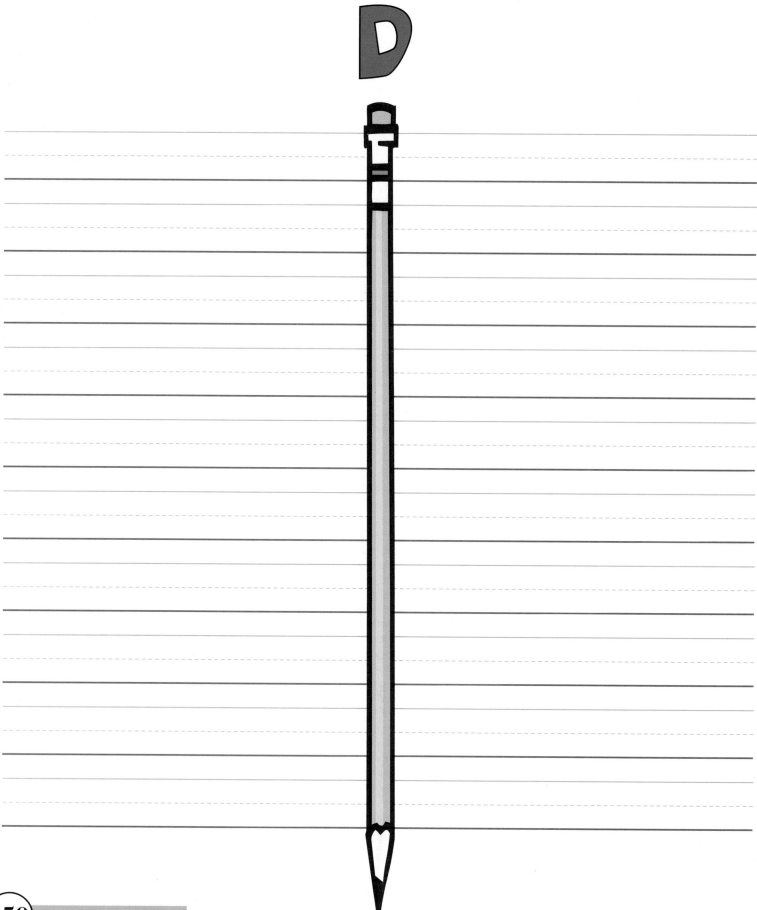

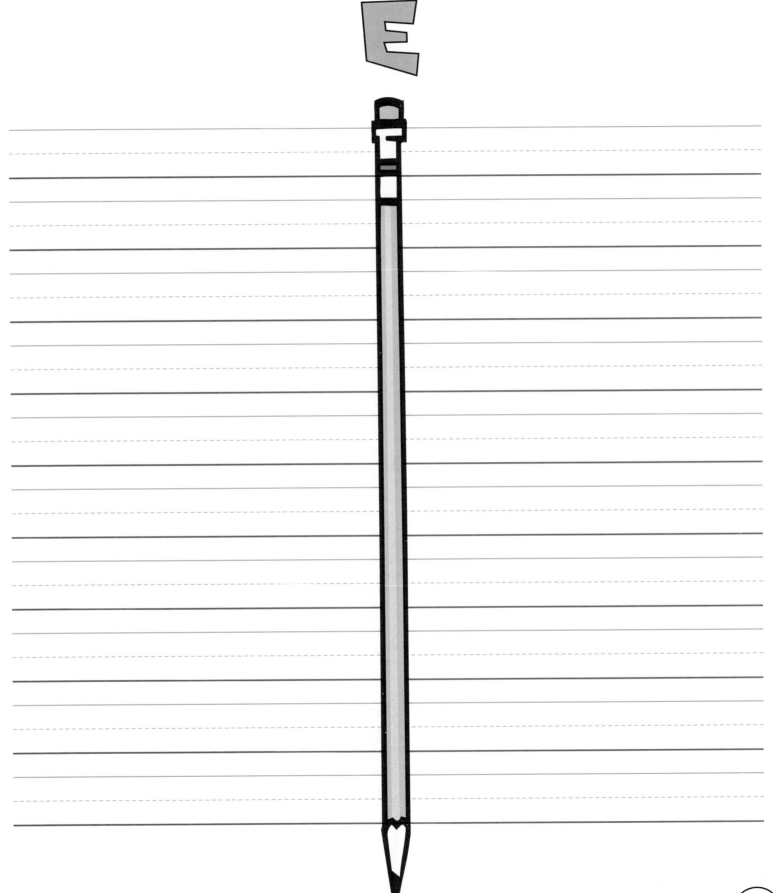

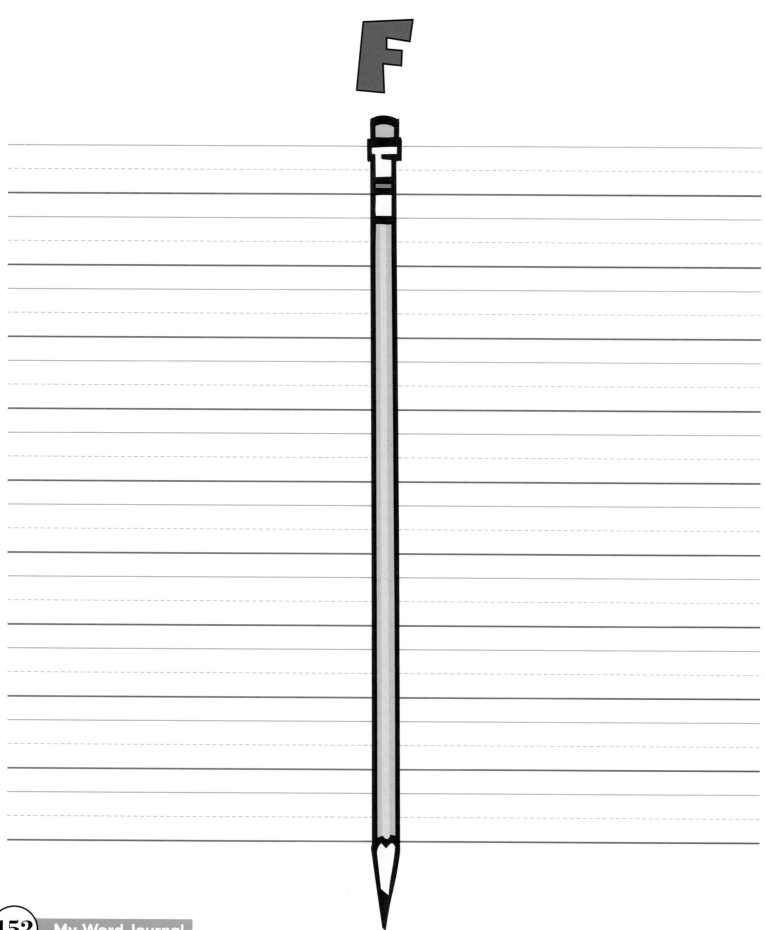

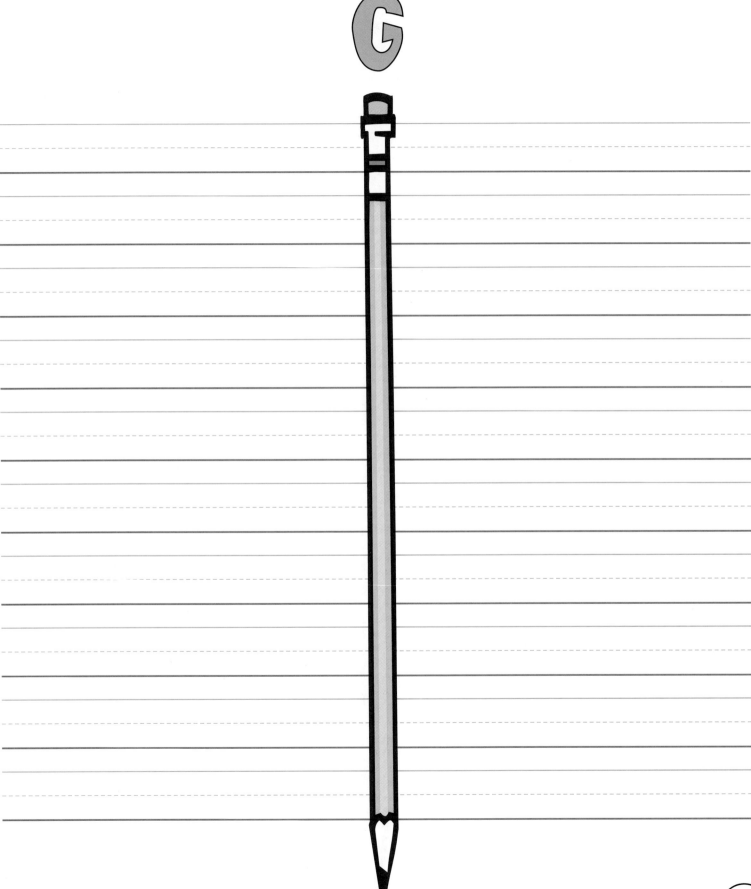

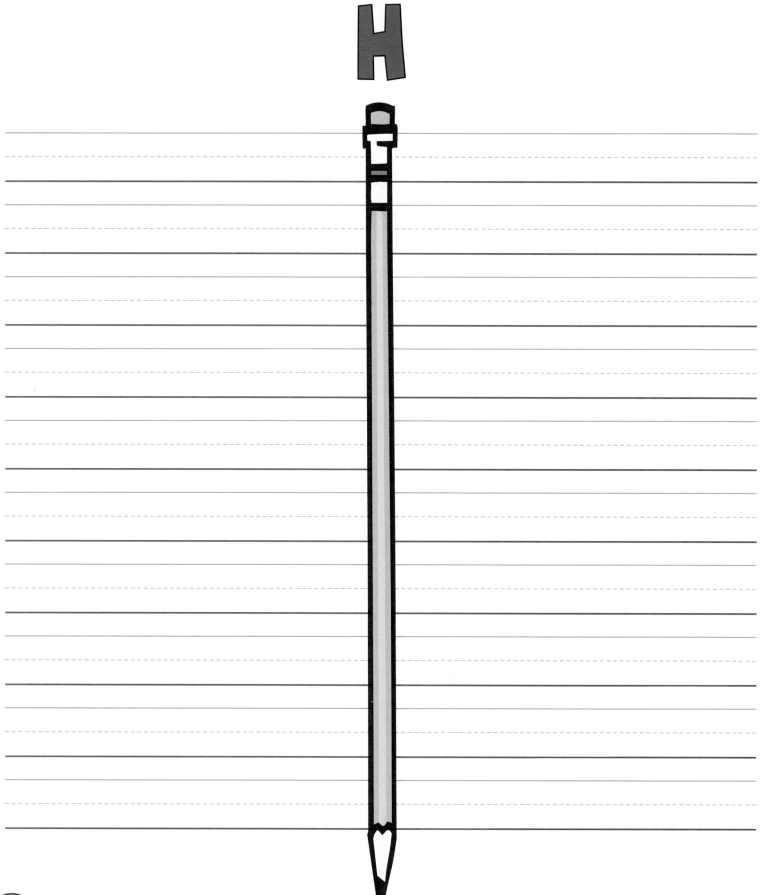

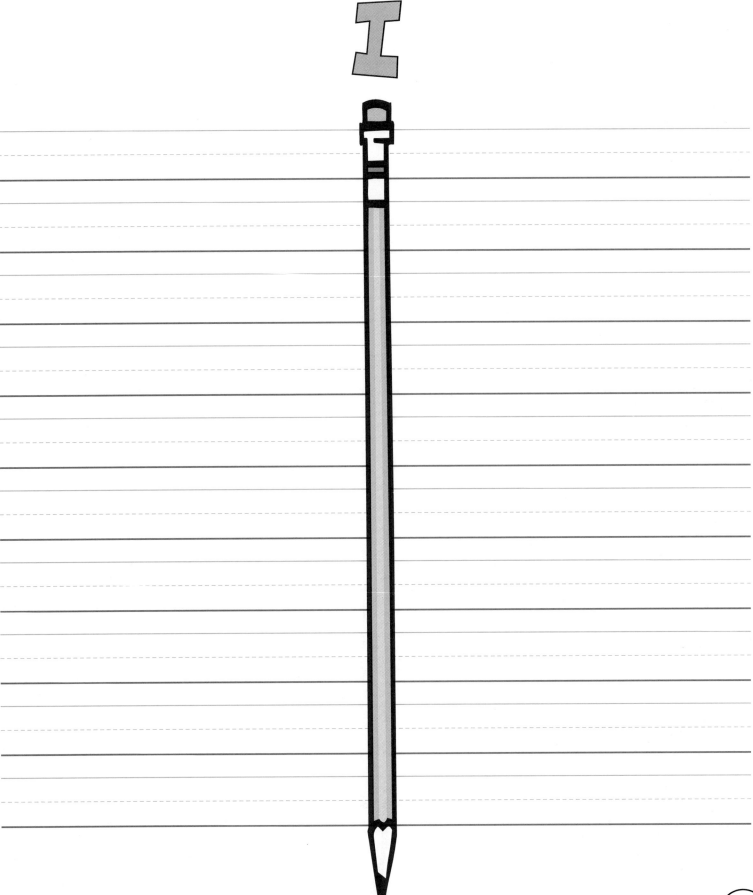

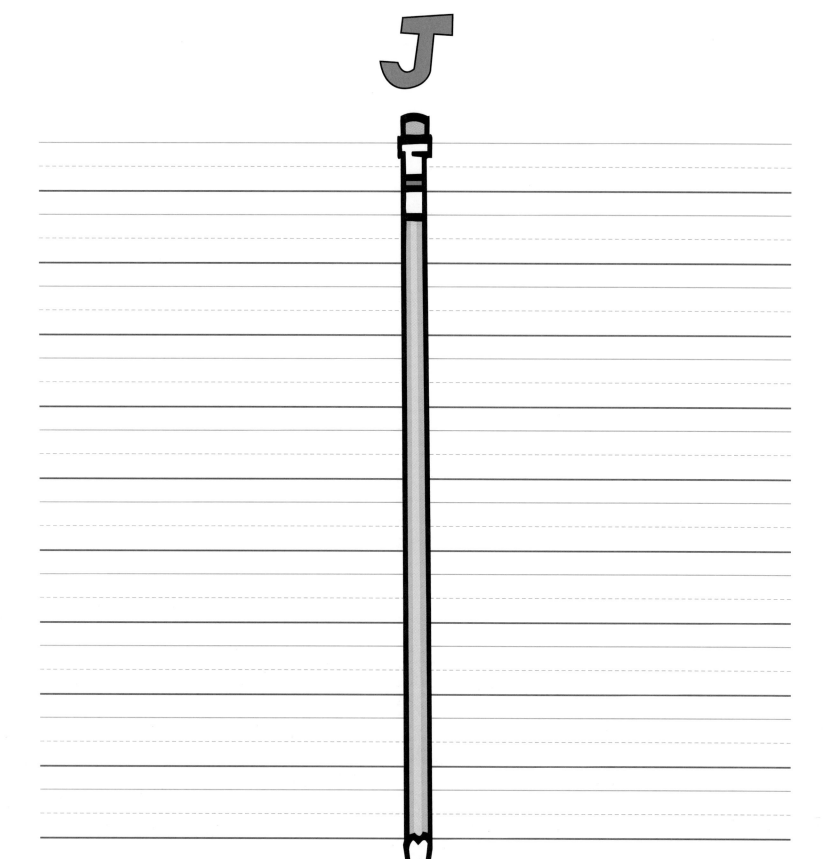

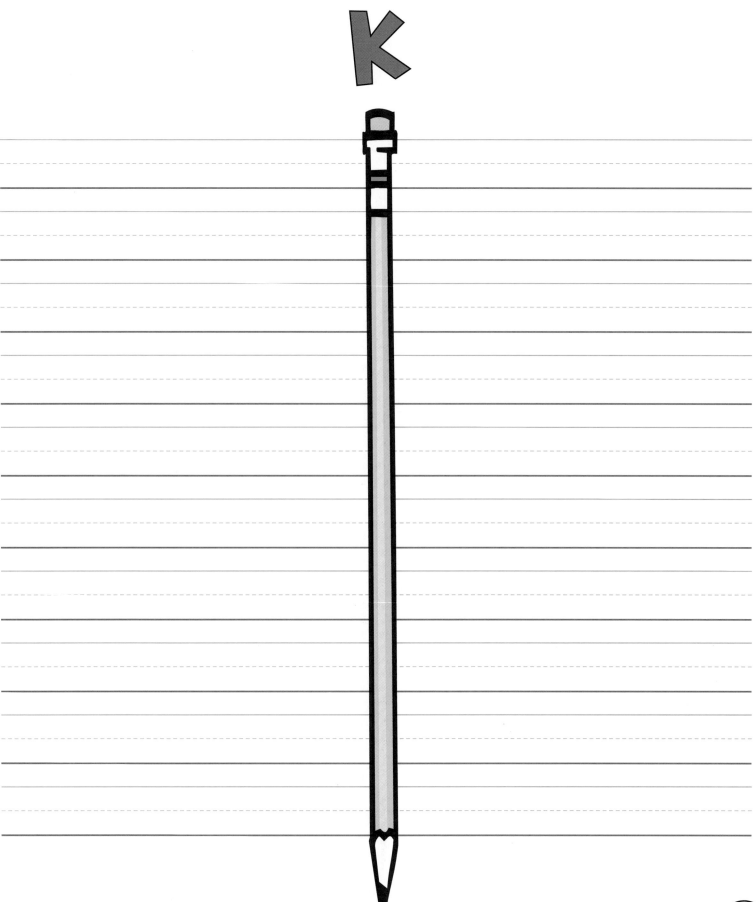

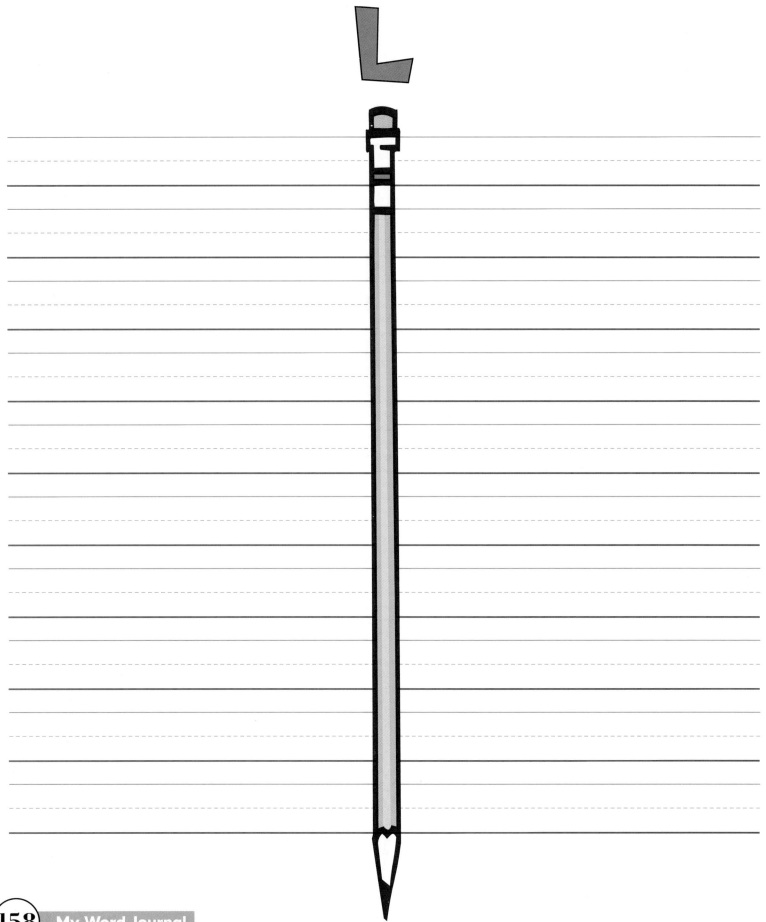

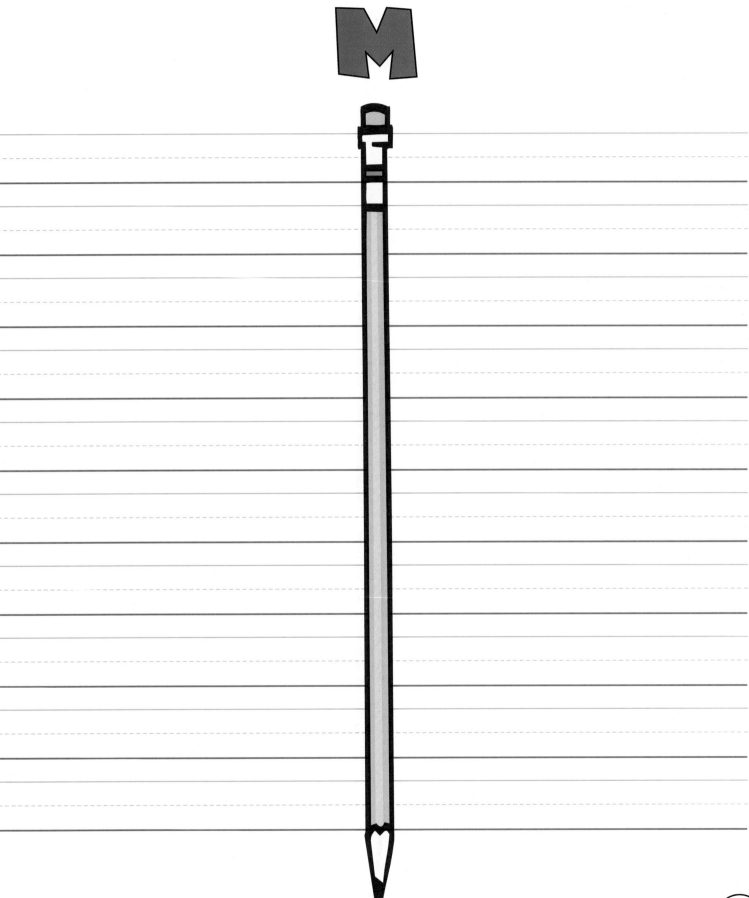

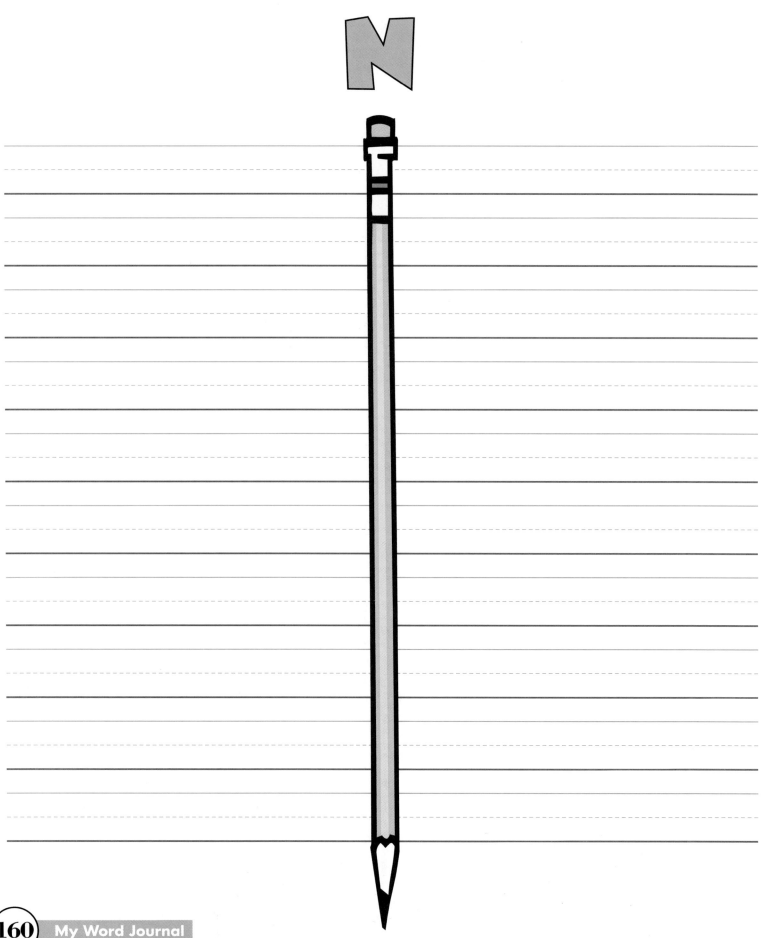

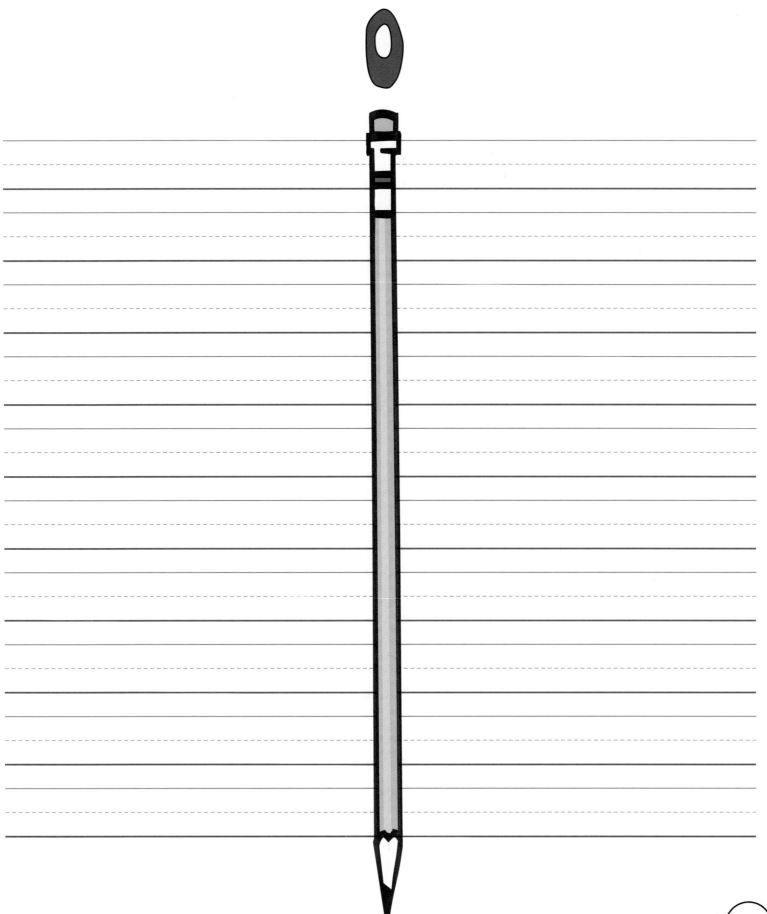

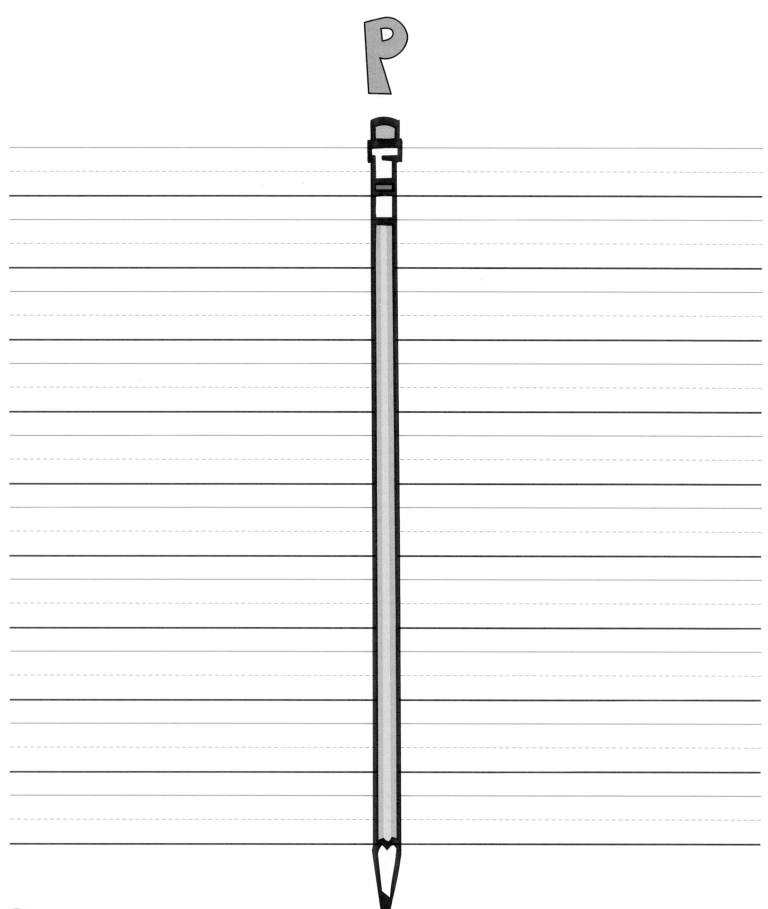

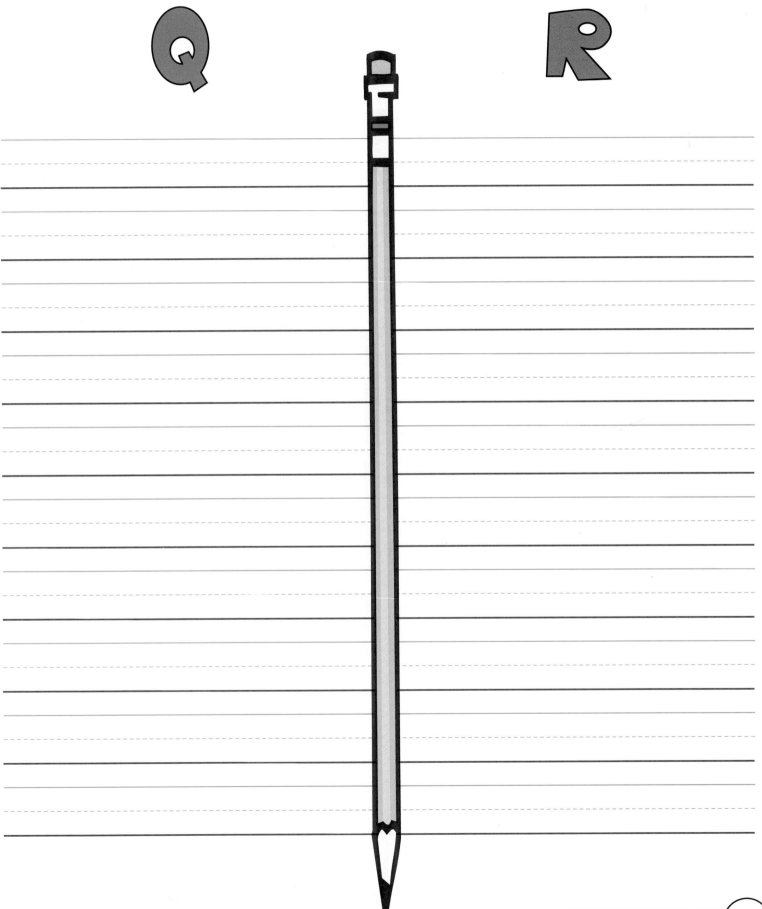

Q

R

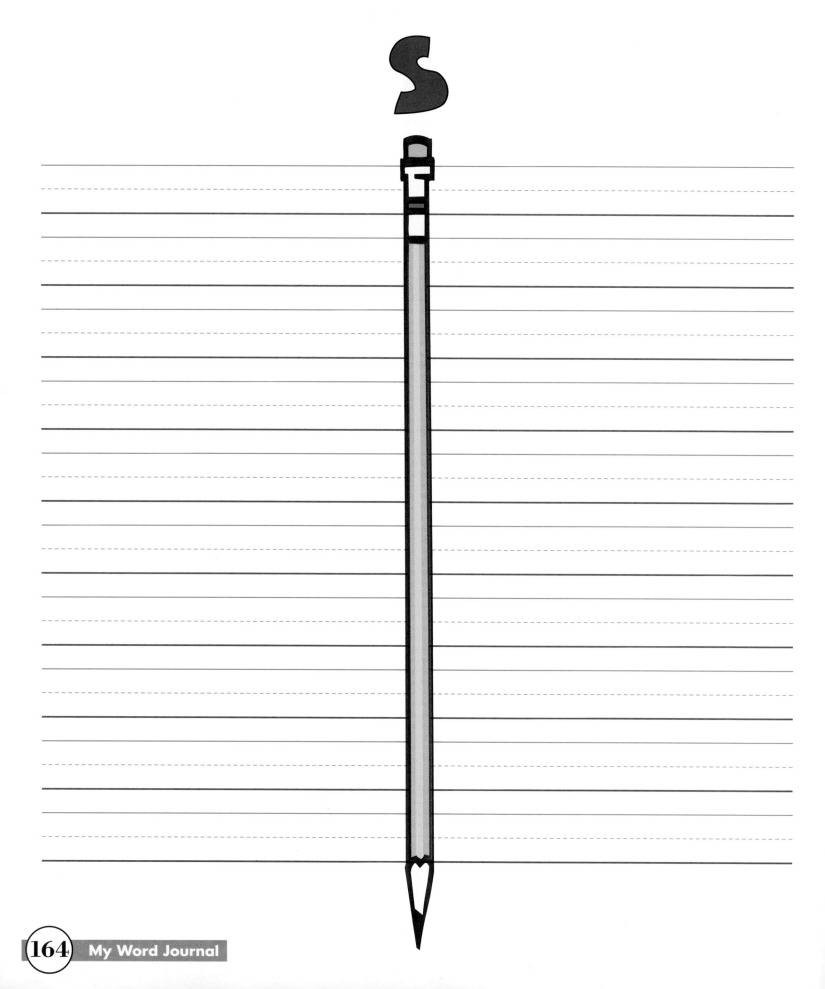

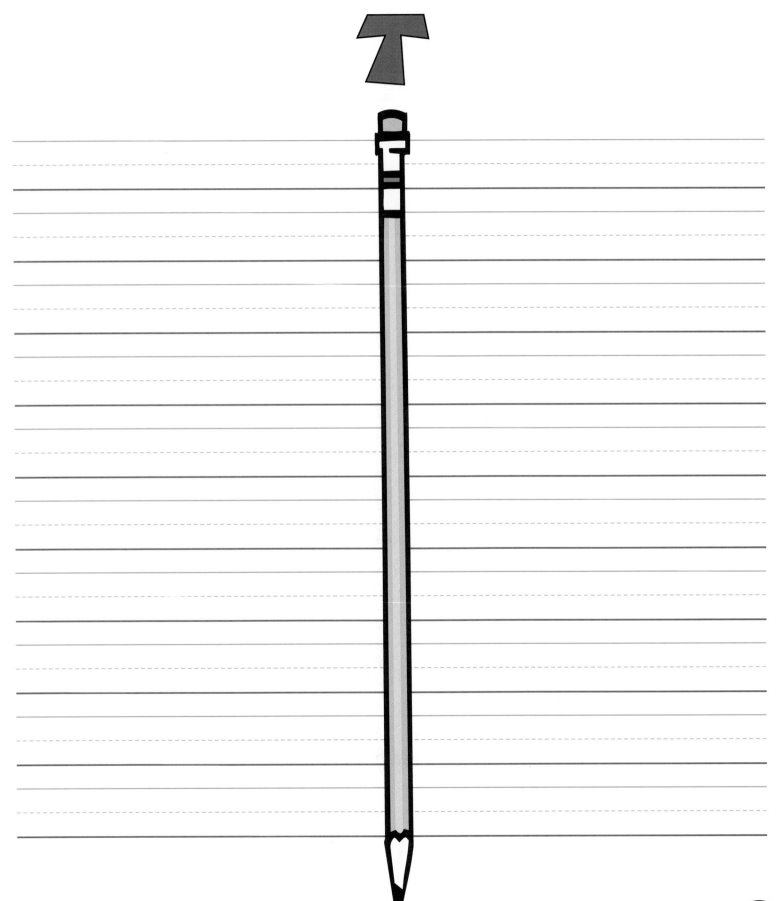

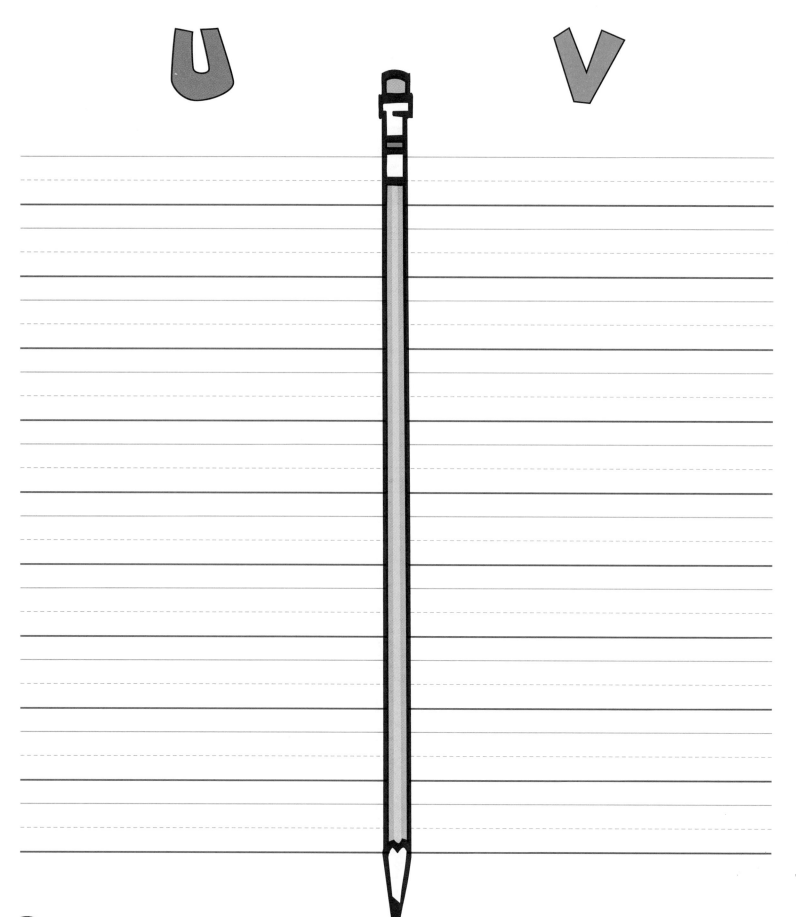

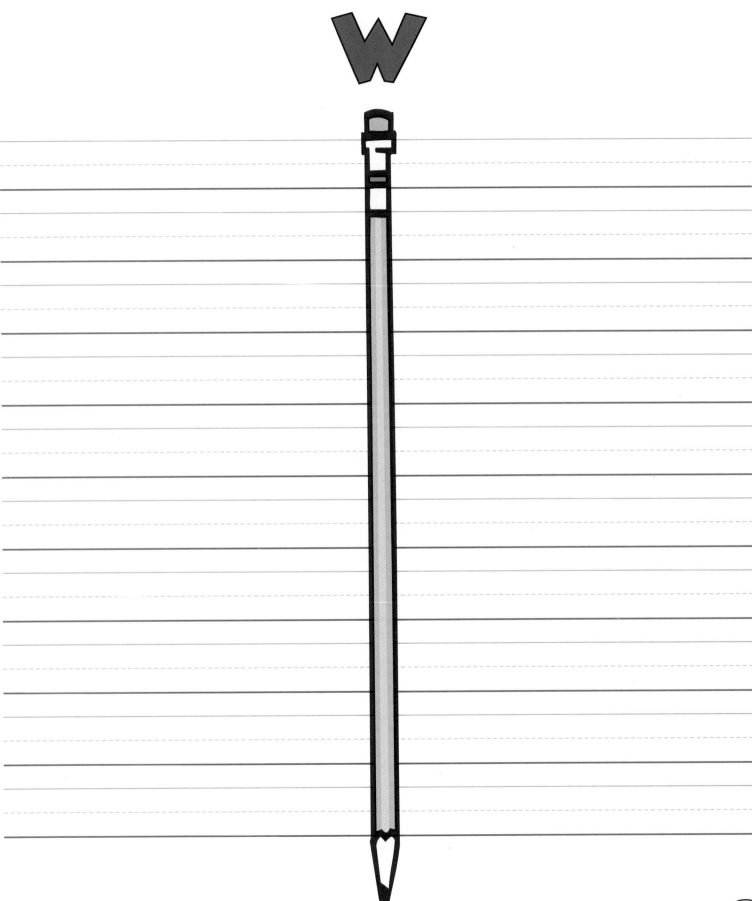

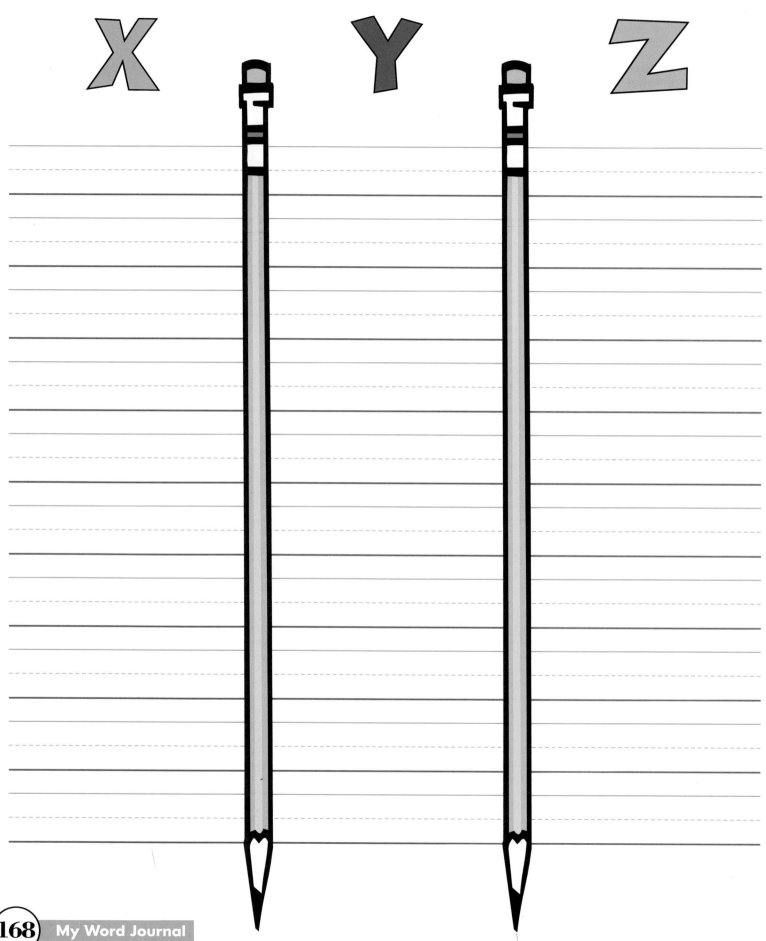

HELPER PAGES

If you forget how to use the Spelling Study Strategy
or one of the activities on your learning plan,
just look it up in the **Helper Pages**.

Checking a Test Letter by Letter

1 Get out your pen, this week's spelling list, and the test you want to check.

2 Put the first word on the test paper next to the first word on the spelling list. Check the spelling one letter at a time. If the word is spelled wrong, circle it and write the correct spelling next to the mistake.

3 Keep going until you have checked all the words.

Spelling Test Tips
Look & Listen/Write & Check

1 **Look** at the speaker. Looking at the speaker helps you get ready to write.

2 **Listen** carefully so you hear the word correctly.

3 **Write** the word clearly with a pencil so your writing will be easy to read.

4 **Check** your spelling.

Taking a Self-Test

1. Look quickly at the first word on your list.

   Cover the word.

   Write the word on a piece of scrap paper.

2. Do this for each word on your list.

3. Use your spelling list to check your test.

4. Write the correct spelling next to any word you did not spell correctly.

Taking a Practice Test

1. Find a partner.

2. Give your partner your spelling list. Ask your partner to tell you if he or she cannot read a word on your list. Say the word.

3. Ask your partner to read all of the words on your list out loud, one at a time.

4. Write each word on a piece of scrap paper.

5. Use your list to correct your own practice test. Write the correct spelling next to any word you did not spell correctly.

Flip Folder

1. Get a **Flip Folder** and a **Flip Folder Practice Sheet**.

2. Print the spelling words you want to practice in the first column. It is **very important** to make sure your spelling is correct.

3. Slide your practice sheet into the **Flip Folder**.

4. Open Flap 1. Look at the first word. Say the word. (You may want to spell the word to yourself.)

5. Close Flap 1. See the word in your mind. (You may want to close your eyes.)

6. Open Flap 2. Write the word on the paper.

7. Open Flap 1 and Flap 2 at the same time. Check your spelling.

8. Close the flaps.

9. Open Flap 3. Write the word again.

10. Open Flap 1 and Flap 3 at the same time. Check your spelling.

Spelling Tic-Tac-Toe

1. Trade spelling lists with a partner. Make sure you can read each other's words.

2. Draw a tic-tac-toe board on a piece of scrap paper or the chalkboard.

3. Decide who will go first. Decide who will use **X** and who will use **O**.

4. Say the first word on your partner's list. Your partner should spell the word out loud while you check the spelling. If your partner is correct, your partner should write **X** or **O,** whichever he or she is using, on the tic-tac-toe board. If your partner misses the word, spell the word out loud for your partner.

5. Trade jobs. Your partner will say the first word on your list. If you spell it correctly, make an **X** or an **O**. If you are not correct, your partner will spell the word out loud for you.

6. Keep playing until you or your partner makes three **X**'s or **O**'s in a line on the board. If no one makes a line of **X**'s or **O**'s, start again.

Word Sort Sheets

Word sorts help you group words by the sounds you hear and the spelling patterns you see in each word. You can do word sorts by yourself or with a partner.

Follow these steps to do a word sort by yourself:

1. Get the **Word Sort Sheet** for the spelling unit you are studying. Cut apart the words on the sheet. If you want to do a word sort for a lesson that does not have a **Word Sort Sheet,** write each word on an index card or on a small piece of scrap paper.

2. Look at each word. Say each word.

3. Use the sounds you hear and the spelling patterns you see to match each word to a **Master Word**.

4. If a word doesn't fit, put it under the question mark (**?**).

5. Keep going until you have sorted all your words. If you can, write other words that fit the sort on pieces of paper. Add them to the word sort.

To do a word sort with a partner, follow the same steps but take turns saying the words to each other.

Word Hunter

① Look around for words you don't know how to spell.

② Write the word you want to learn in **My Word Journal**.

③ Check letter by letter to make sure you wrote the word right. Use a dictionary or ask your teacher to check your spelling.

HANDWRITING HINTS

To the student: Good handwriting makes your correct spelling easier to read. Use these **Handwriting Hints** as you practice your words.

UNIT 1 Handwriting is better if you hold your pencil correctly.

left-handed   **right-handed**

UNIT 2 Manuscript letters should be vertical (straight up and down). This shows the correct way to position your paper to help keep your letters straight.

left-handed   **right-handed**

UNIT 3 Your letters will be straight up and down if you:

1. Position your paper correctly.

2. Pull all downstrokes in the proper direction.

3. Shift your paper as you write.

UNIT 4 Write **hold, gold,** and **fold**. Are all of your letters straight up and down? Put an **X** under each letter that is not straight. Practice these letters.

UNIT 5 Start a backward circle at three o'clock. Practice making backward circles on your paper.

UNIT 6 — Use backward circles to write the letters **a, d, g, o,** and **q**. Write the word **today**. Write an **X** under the backward circles.

UNIT 7 — You use a "slide right" straight line — to write lowercase **e**. Practice making the "slide right" line.

UNIT 8 — If you make a good **c** after the "slide right," — e your **e** will be good.

UNIT 9 — Write these words in ABC order: **store, been, were**. Now check to see if you wrote **e** well.

UNIT 10 — Start forward circles at nine o'clock. Practice making forward circles on your paper.

UNIT 11 — Use forward circles to write **b** and **p**. Write **bright** and **sleep**. Write an **X** under the forward circles.

UNIT 12 — Write **hop, robe,** and **globe**. Draw a line under the letters that have the most complete circles.

UNIT 13 — Write an uppercase **S** and a lowercase **s**. 8 s Draw a circle over the top part of each letter and another circle over the bottom part.

UNIT 14 — Write **myself, saw,** and **was**. Draw a line under the best **s** and an **X** under the one that you want to make better next time.

UNIT 15 — There should be a one-finger space between words. Write a sentence using at least three spelling words. Check the spacing.

This is good spacing.

UNIT 16   Write **snow, pin,** and **slam**. Are the "pull strokes" straight in **n** and **m**? Practice writing **n** and **m** until you are happy with them.

UNIT 17   Write **blue** and **glass**. blue glass Does your spacing look like this?

UNIT 18   Practice writing these consonant blends: **br, dr, fr,** and **gr**. Check your spacing.

UNIT 19   If your **r**'s look like this, ⌐, be more careful. Stop before you push up (retrace). Write **far, corn,** and **part**. Are the **r**'s formed right?

r far corn part

UNIT 20   Write your spelling words. Check the retraces h r in **h** and **r**.

UNIT 21   When you write **k,** be sure to stop after the second stroke or your letter will look like this: k .

UNIT 22   Write a sentence using as many of your spelling words as you can. Check the spacing between words.

UNIT 23   The letters **a, c, e, g, m, n, o, p, q, r, s, u, v, w, x, y,** and **z** are called short letters. They reach only to the middle of the line: a . Write your spelling words. Circle the short letters.

UNIT 24   The letters **i, j,** and **t** should reach just beyond the middle of the line: t . These letters are called middle letters. Write **father** and **sister**. Are your middle letters the right size?

UNIT 25 The letters **b, d, f, h, k,** and **l** are called tall letters. They should reach the top of the line: b . Write your spelling words. Draw an **X** under the tall letters.

UNIT 26 Write a sentence using some spelling words. Draw a line under words that have all the letters written correctly. Circle letters you want to improve.

UNIT 27 Write your spelling words. Count the circle letters (**a, b, d, g, o, p, q**) in each word.

UNIT 28 We use slanted lines \ / to write the letters **v, y, w, k, x,** and **z**. Write these letters carefully.

UNIT 29 Some letters go below the baseline: y . The letters **j, g, p, q,** and **y** are like this. Write **hug, stay,** and **tap** in your best handwriting.

UNIT 30 There should be enough space to put two fingers between sentences. Write two sentences. Check the spacing.

This is a good spacing. It

UNIT 31 The uppercase **C** and lowercase **c** look the same except for the **size** (height). What other letters look the same in uppercase and lowercase except for their **size**?

UNIT 32 Write a sentence that tells why good handwriting is important. Use your best handwriting.

SPELLING AND HANDWRITING

Good handwriting makes it easier for others to understand your good ideas.

Letter	Common problem	Incorrect letter form makes word appear misspelled	Correct
o	OPEN	dóll	doll
n	LETTER IS NOT COMPLETE	r'ow	now
e	NO SLIDE RIGHT STROKE	c'ar	ear
a	OPEN	fár	far

Manuscript Alphabet

Aa Bb Cc Dd Ee Ff

Gg Hh Ii Jj Kk Ll

Mm Nn Oo Pp Qq

Rr Ss Tt Uu Vv

Ww Xx Yy Zz